WHAT
YOUR BRIGHT
CHILD
CAN'T SEE

SECRETS
TO CONQUERING
LEARNING DIFFICULTIES

DR. LOU SPINOZZI

LIFESUCCESS PUBLISHING, LLC
8900 E Pinnacle Peak Road, Suite D240
Scottsdale, AZ 85255

Telephone:	800.473.7134
Fax:	480.661.1014

E-mail:	admin@lifesuccesspublishing.com
ISBN:	1-59930-033-8
Cover & Layout:	Chris Mackey & LifeSuccess Publishing

COMPANIES, ORGANIZATIONS, INSTITUTIONS, AND INDUSTRY
PUBLICATIONS: Quantity discounts are available on bulk purchases of
this book for reselling, educational purposes, subscription incentives, gifts,
sponsorship, or fundraising. Special books or book excerpts can also be created
to fit specific needs such as private labeling with your logo on the cover and a
message from a VIP printed inside. For more information please contact our
Special Sales Department at LifeSuccess Publishing.

PRAISE FOR WHAT YOUR BRIGHT CHILD CAN'T SEE

I have had the pleasure of helping children with learning challenges for 38 years. I am totally impressed and excited with the breakthrough Dr. Lou Spinozzi has made in this area. If your child is having learning difficulties, you owe it to yourself and your child to thoroughly investigate Dr. Spinozzi's wonderful work. Your child's bright future depends on it. His work will change your child's life.

Bob Proctor,
Chairman, LifeSuccess Productions

I think a light bulb will go on for many parents when they realize that reading skills depend on more than just 20/20 vision. It actually brought tears to my eyes remembering the struggles I had with Connor and the profound relief I felt when his problem was finally diagnosed. A copy of this book should be mandatory in every school! It offers so much valuable information in language that everyone can understand—a great service that can help so many parents and children live a better life.

Pam Carballido,
Mother of a Vision Therapy Graduate

Dr. Louis Spinozzi has contributed a valuable addition to the resources available for parents on vision development and how developmental optometry can help. I believe that those who take the time to read this book will better understand the worth of a proper vision evaluation and how Vision Therapy can improve a child's ability to function academically and behaviorally.

Patricia S. Lemer, M.Ed., NCC,
Executive Director, Developmental Delay Registry

In What Your Bright Child Can't See, Dr. Spinozzi has told a story that needs to be told over and over again. Educators have been faced with the complex problems of children with learning disabilities for many years.

Dr. Spinozzi has clearly indicated the possibility of a vision problem beyond visual acuity which could be present. He has taken his passion for helping children to achieve at a higher level to the point of a simple understanding of the visual process, often overlooked by teachers, pediatricians and other vision specialists. He presents powerful examples of typical vision problems which can lead to devastating social disadvantages.

A wide distribution of this special work on vision and its potential by Dr. Spinozzi will touch the lives of many who will gain a better understanding of vision and its possible effect on learning and behavior.

Alvin Levin, O.D., F.A.A.O., CAE,
Past President, American Optometric Association

While discussing What Your Bright Child Can't See with Dr. Spinozzi, I realized that members of my own family—including myself—fit the picture he describes. His approach and findings make sense. The coordination of clinical signs and symptoms with the physiology and anatomy involved offer a refreshing and dynamic solution for children with vision-related learning problems.

Dr. Frank Sargent, MD

As a nurse and a homeschool mother whose child has completed a Vision Therapy program, I am not only enthusiastic about Vision Therapy and the benefits my child obtained from it, but I am also excited that this book will be available for all those parents who search for answers and cannot readily find them.

Dr. Spinozzi has explained vision-related learning problems and their solutions in an easy-to-understand text that I know will become a much needed resource for parents, educators, and physicians. I am excited that "the secret" will finally become a common understanding which will in turn, help many more parents and children. Now that my son is a sophomore in college, I can safely say that vision therapy is one of the two key events that shaped and prepared him for college and his direction in life, without which he would not be who he is today.

Ronnie McKay, RN,
Mother of Vision Therapy Graduate

WHAT
YOUR BRIGHT
CHILD
CAN'T SEE

SECRETS
TO CONQUERING LEARNING DIFFICULTIES

DEDICATION

To my wonderful family; my wife Lynn, and our children David and Dominic;

To the special people who helped me find success during my formative education years:

Mom and Dad, for the importance you placed on a good education;
Mrs. Griffith, second and third grade classroom teacher;
Major Pujans and Captain Muzi, leaders at Valley Forge Military Academy;
Dr. Ken Walker, college friend and mentor;
Dr. James Bosse, graduate school friend and mentor;

Thanks to all of you for your friendships, belief, guidance and encouragement.

To the children, adults and families who are searching for secrets to conquering their learning difficulties.

TABLE OF CONTENTS

FOREWORD
BY JOYCE INOUYE

The book you're holding has the power to change your life and the life of your child, just as my life changed when I discovered the secret of vision therapy.

As a specialist in learning disabilities for over 28 years, I have had the privilege of helping clients of all ages unlock their potential. Sharing their victories, both large and small, I have been blessed to see their lives change. Yet, there was a time in my life when, despite my education and credentials, despite my awards and merits, and despite my experience in teaching those with special needs in all grades, I found myself unable to help my own son.

You see, Garrett had learning-related vision problems, and I understand on a very personal level the heartache that a family experiences when their child is having difficulty in school because of them.

When my son was in the third grade, he was reading isolated words at grade level. His reading comprehension was that of a tenth grader, but Garrett's reading fluency was staggered and did not match his ability. When he read, Garrett would have difficulty keeping his place. He would misread words or guess with similar words that would work in context. He learned to answer questions by deductive reasoning and had to work very hard to attain, and retain, his honors standing.

My background in learning disabilities enabled me to diagnose his visual difficulties, to work through them, and to help him find greater success using accommodations and learning strategies, but I simply couldn't increase his ability to fluently read the printed word.

Although Garrett's report card reflected his dedication and diligence, his self-esteem wavered in the fourth grade. He doubted his gifted abilities because he read with limited fluency.

I knew Garrett had a visual processing problem, although two reputable optometrists thought otherwise. The doctors prescribed glasses to no avail, and when I persisted by asking questions about vision therapy, the doctors were dismissive. I became confused with their reaction and doubted that vision therapy was the answer to Garrett's problem.

Although disappointed that vision professionals couldn't help Garrett, I was heartbroken as my son's self-esteem spiraled downward. I knew that he was very bright and also knew that there had to be something more that could help him. I continued my search, deciding to independently study vision therapy. I bought the textbooks that the Fullerton School of Optometry used to teach vision therapy to its students. The material was thought provoking, but I was still unsure.

Shortly thereafter, my worldview underwent a seismic shift. I happened to meet a world-renowned developmental optometrist at a conference at which we both were speaking. In between our seminars, I talked with him about my experiences with optometrists who did not believe in vision therapy. He said that although his studies demonstrated the efficacy of vision therapy, the techniques were not being taught or practiced in clinical settings.

After our discussion, I felt hope for the first time. I took Garrett to the developmental optometrist's office for testing where he was diagnosed with convergence insufficiency and a visual processing dysfunction. I felt validated, as I had been convinced for some time that my son had a visual processing problem.

I enrolled Garrett in a six-month program of vision therapy with a challenge to the developmental optometrist that if vision therapy worked, he would have his greatest advocate but if vision therapy did not work, I would announce the fallacy of it.

I can vividly remember that after two months of therapy, Garrett turned to me in church one morning as we sang and said, "Mom, I think vision therapy is working! I can keep up in the hymnal!" I stood there, tears welling up in my eyes and thought, "Those eye exercises changed his visual processing?" Apparently, they did. His progress in oral reading was quickly recognized at school, and Garrett was placed in the advanced reading group. My heart swelled as I saw Garrett choosing to read books in his free time.

After three months, Garrett was re-tested by the developmental optometrist. We discovered that the in-office vision therapy and home exercises had trained Garrett to perceive correctly, and his difficulties with reading fluency were gone.

Garrett knew his vision exercises had worked, and many times I found him doing them for fun. Since he did not have any other specific learning challenges, vision therapy was the key to unlocking Garrett's potential. It allowed him the life-changing joy of reading with ease and blessed me with the opportunity to witness his world open up.

Today, Garrett is 19 years old and an avid reader. He graduated from high school as an International Baccalaureate candidate with honors. During his senior year, Garrett attests to have easily read over 10,000 pages even with the academic load of six Advanced

Placement classes. Reading books and novels was something I would find him doing in what little free time he had.

He currently attends Westmont College in Santa Barbara with intentions to pursue his doctorate in Biblical Counseling where surfing now competes with reading as his favorite pastime.

Learning difficulties are like a jigsaw puzzle in which the student, family members, teachers, and specialists search for a solution. Working together in a team effort, they can discover the unique design of the puzzle and how to best fit the pieces together.

In this book, Dr. Louis Spinozzi presents facts that bring direction, clarification, understanding and affirmation to those, and to the families of those, with learning-related vision problems. This book would have made my journey with Garrett so much shorter and much less heart wrenching.

On behalf of the families whose lives will be directed and transformed by this book, I express my deep gratitude to Dr. Spinozzi for creating this comprehensive resource and for unveiling the secret solution to vision dysfunctions that adversely effect learning.

It is my hope and prayer that this transformational book will ease the feelings of hopelessness and desperation that children and parents feel and bring the knowledge that vision therapy can unlock the potential in individuals.

With a passion to share the truth and bring hope to those with learning-related vision learning problems,

Joyce Inouye M.A. Ed.
Specialist in Learning Disabilities
www. ChildD.org
Christian Educational Therapy
La Habra, California

Joyce Inouye's extensive background in special education, and work with learning challenged individuals, involves 29 years of teaching students in every grade through public, private and specialized schools. In her tenure she taught graduate courses at La Verne University in "Assessment and Curriculum Development" for those graduate students seeking a future in teaching those with learning challenges. She continues to teach and train parents, teachers, administrators, and professionals in the fields of pediatrics, neurology, psychology and counseling. Joyce is renowned in Southern California for her service in support of Christian schools in the Association of Christian Schools International. She provides psycho-educational testing, consulting, and specialized educational therapy to those who want to draw from her expertise through her private practice of Christian Educational Therapy.

A NOTE FROM THE AUTHOR

Do you know any parents who are convinced that their children are bright, yet frustrated by their inexplicable difficulties in the classroom? Typically, these otherwise bright children have trouble reading, writing, spelling, and processing information. Their grades in school are lackluster, or perhaps they work extremely hard to achieve a "B" average. In many cases, "C's" and "D's" are more common.

These children are astute in other aspects of their lives, but schoolwork takes an unusually long time to finish while homework is a battleground full of tears, resistance, and frustration. Teachers use all of the educational training and research they have learned or encountered over the years to try and help these children perform to their potential. Parents hire tutors, lobby the schools for special classes and additional help, and take their children to pediatricians for testing. Some even bring their children to other entities hoping that one test or one enlightened professional will be able to come up with a diagnosis and a solution to their problem.

As time goes on, the answer is not forthcoming and children start to internalize the problems they are having. And as a result, their self-esteem becomes fleeting or non-existent. Parents face days of discouragement and fatigue as their patience wears thin and resources are exhausted.

It has long been a passion of mine to help these parents and children. I have had the privilege to do so on a smaller scale throughout the last thirty years in my Developmental and Behavioral Optometric practice. However, as I work with children, counsel with parents, and speak to professionals at schools, I have realized that there is a specific need to carry my mission one step further: get the word out to parents and educators who are struggling with these issues on a daily basis, but are missing information about the critical link between vision and learning.

The good news is that help is available for these children. Many of them are dealing with vision or vision processing related learning difficulties or delays. Many of these problems go undiagnosed and, therefore, untreated.

Vision incorporates three basic abilities:

> Seeing clearly, or 20/20 visual acuity (eyesight);
>
> Using the muscles of the eyes to work together (eye teaming); and
>
> Taking information in the brain and integrating it with the other senses (visual processing).

Most people are familiar only with acuity. However, an estimated astonishing 25% of children are affected by difficulty with the teaming or brain processing aspects of vision. Most take these areas for granted when they assume vision is only a matter of clear eyesight.

A major portion of the information that we absorb for learning to take place comes to us through our vision. If our eyes are not "teaming" properly, then the information we take in will be blurry or indistinct and incorrect in other ways. It is a constant struggle to process what is seen when the clues are incorrect.

My goal for this book is to create a resource for concerned parents and educators, one that answers questions in a way that can easily be understood. Many times, parents of the children I am working with voice the same frustrations: "Why didn't I know about this?" And "I went to the library and looked for information under "Learning Difficulties" and could not find anything related to vision problems." This is because the information is often misunderstood and, consequently, misinterpreted.

Often, when children have clear eyesight, or 20/20 vision, adults assume that there is nothing wrong with vision, and the true cause for their difficulties remains hidden. Left untreated, vision problems can further impede children's development and academic performance. Teachers or parents can misinterpret symptoms as commonly known behavioral disorders. This unfortunate situation also results in children's true difficulties being undiagnosed and untreated. Sometimes, medication prescribed for the misdiagnosed behavioral disorder will temporarily improve some of the symptoms, but the real cause of the difficulty still exists and otherwise bright children will still function at a level less than where they could potentially be.

I was one of these children. I know what it feels like to be behind and the oddball of the class. I know the frustration associated with many aspects of learning-related vision problems all too well. But I also know the freedom and opportunity that knowledge and education can offer a suffering child and his or her family.

Most never know the havoc a poorly functioning vision system can wreak on children's lives. Athletics, peer groups, confidence, grades, college opportunities, careers, and family relations: all of these and many more are acutely influenced by individuals' vision systems whether healthy or problematic. Only after children's faulty vision systems are corrected can the haze of confusion and frustration be lifted and drastic changes occur in life.

Perhaps you are looking for the missing piece to the puzzle, whether it is for your child, your student, or even yourself. As you read this book, you'll discover the answers to your most pressing questions and share the life-changing experiences of those who have put these solutions to work. You'll learn simple ways to test yourself or anyone for signs of visual teaming difficulties, and where to turn when you're ready to take the next step and start applying the solutions in your own life.

What matters most is that you'll find the knowledge you need to forever change the future of the one for whom you care so much. My hope is that this invaluable, transforming information inspires you to set your child on a path to fully functioning vision and the world of opportunities that good vision can offer.

1 SOMETHING'S WRONG

1 SOMETHING'S WRONG

Vision. What children see is important. As parents, we point out the fire truck as it whizzes along the street, and all the brightly colored blossoms in our neighbor's garden. We also shield their eyes from violent television programs and even some of the morning cartoons. Their eyes allow them to absorb what our lives are all about. We want them to see the world.

Even more important than what their gaze is fixed upon is how our children are seeing. We take for granted that what we see is truth, that what we see is real. What if our children's eyes deceived them? What if their eyes played tricks on them? Sadly, this happens often, and even the children are unaware.

Vision is a complex process that involves over 20 visual skills in addition to visual acuity. In our society many lack awareness that we actually have a visual system, not just eyeballs. Parents and educators are often uninformed about the important role vision plays in academic, social, business, personal, and even athletic success. Children's future life endeavors rely on a visual system that is functioning correctly. And if their vision systems are faulty, the dysfunction is not recognized or treated until late in the game.

Many educators, doctors and parents feel that something is wrong, but are knocked off the path to true discovery by certain catchphrases or an abundance of misdiagnoses. Families are led on a wild goose chase as they search for the "one thing" that will work for their child. Everyone is frustrated.

As parents, we almost take vision for granted. When our children line up to have their vision screened as preschoolers, and even in years after that, we, as parents, eagerly await the pronouncement of "20/20 Vision". Seeing "20/20" is only half of the battle, but we assume it is everything.

And if an eyesight issue is detected, we know that doctors can prescribe glasses and contacts. If there is a problem with your child's eyesight, just slipping the corrective lenses on over the eye can instantaneously improve eyesight almost to "perfection." Truly, that is no small feat. To see clearly with the aid of any kind of lens is miraculous. However, there could be other problems lurking beneath the surface of your child's iris.

This is the crux of the vision situation: even children with "perfect eyesight" can experience visual disorders manifesting as what appear to be behavioral problems, laziness, confusion, lack of effort, or just plain not getting it. Even the brightest of children can experience reading a simple book as slow and tedious, perhaps not even being able to get through a straightforward assignment. In fact, the majority of these situations are not discovered until much later because children mask their difficulties.

Our children do not notice what is missing. How can they? Chances are they cannot recognize their own problem. They have nothing with which to compare their poor vision. Only after a sequence of low grades catches the attention of the concerned parent, or perhaps a teacher's keen intuition suggests there must be something wrong, do these real problems surface. These bright children who would otherwise sail through homework and tests find themselves at the beginning of underachievement.

Imagine children's frustration and disappointment. Certainly, they must know something is wrong, right? Imagine the parents' frustration and disappointment. My bet is that you see some kind of trouble. Both sets of individuals may second-guess their abilities and question their now shaky confidence. What is the missing piece to this puzzle?

But there is an answer. The key to finding it lies in understanding a child's unique vision system. Seeing the letters on the page or an object clearly is the first step. Following a moving target, like a ball or a line of print is yet another step. The next step is the one that most people take for granted and don't even associate with the vision system, and that is interpreting correctly that which you are seeing. For example, how do you know where to stand so you can catch a ball? You have to process the visual information to make a decision and then move your body based on that information. In clinical terms, more than clear eyesight (seeing "20/20"), good vision is the result of healthy eyes, excellent acuity, efficient oculomotor skills, intricate processing, and the integration of all these systems; bottom line, vision is a complex process.

Because people assume that the only visual skill a child needs is to be able to see "20/20", parents go on an endless search to uncover the source of their children's struggles. It can't be something as easily recognizable as vision, can it? So, parents, teachers, grandparents, tutors spend hours and even years seeking the answer to this question, sometimes never finding it. Clearly, the child is bright; surely, he has a bright future ahead of him, too. So what is the problem?

I know parents who have attempted all of the following solutions:

- Spending more one-on-one time with their child during homework sessions;

- Asking teachers to try different teaching techniques;

- Hiring a different tutor;

- Believing that the child just needs to try harder or pay more attention in class;

- Contacting the principal about the teacher's unfair treatment;

- Finding someone to diagnose the child with ADD and prescribe medication.

Do any of these solutions sound familiar to you?

Is homework time a nightmare for your family? Does someone always end up in tears? Does it take three times longer than you think it should? At school, is your child behind? Is he slower than everyone else in spite of extra attention? Is he told to focus, concentrate and try harder?

The truth may lie in a vision system that is not sufficiently and properly developed to be able to successfully accommodate the demands an advanced educational system is making upon it. Flaws within a child's vision system might manifest themselves early in life, or might go unnoticed until the teenage years.

The following is a list of symptoms, any one of which could give us the first clue that a vision problem may be at the root of your child's difficulties. Do you recognize your child here? Is this your child?

1. Skips lines or words while reading or copying

2. Loses place while reading or copying

3. Rereads words or lines

4. Reverses numbers, letters or words

5. Uses a finger or marker to keep place while reading

6. Reads very slowly

7. Has poor reading comprehension

8. Has difficulty remembering what has been read

9. Holds the book closely or writes closely (7-8 inches away)

10. Squints, closes, or covers one eye while reading/ writing

11. Demonstrates unusual posture or head tilt while reading/ writing

12. Experiences headaches

13. Reports eyes hurt or feel tired after a visual task

14. Feels drained or tired after a visual task

15. Reports double vision

16. Says letters or lines "run together" or words "jump"

17. Has poor spelling skills

18. Has handwriting that is crooked or poorly spaced

19. Misaligns letters or numbers

20. Demonstrates unusual clumsiness, poor coordination

21. Has difficulty with sports involving good hand-eye coordination

22. Has an eye that turns in or out

23. Sees more clearly with one eye than the other

24. Feels sleepy while reading

25. Dislikes or avoids tasks requiring sustained concentration

26. Confuses right and left directions

27. Becomes restless at his/her desk

28. Experiences carsickness

29. Demonstrates unusual blinking or eye rubbing

30. Has dry, watery or red eyes

31. Completing homework takes longer than it should

32. Struggles to visualize what was read

Each of the symptoms listed above correlates to one of many different vision problems. Furthermore, each of these symptoms can lead you to the key to a future of success and confidence for your child.

If this book has found its way into your hands, then chances are you have experienced some of the aggravation and defeat that these seemingly minor problems listed above bring along with them. You may be quite aware of the havoc it can wreak on development. You are searching for the one possible answer or the one thing you have not tried. You might be at your wit's end by now or maybe you are just beginning to discover how deeply serious this could be. Something just isn't right, and you know it.

If any of the above symptoms is recognizable in your bright child, then vision therapy may be the missing piece to the puzzle for which you have been searching all along.

My intention for writing this book is twofold: I want to clarify how these behavioral symptoms listed above are related to vision problems. I want these children and even adults who suffer from these symptoms to rest knowing there is effective treatment that changes lives. I want parents, other health care professionals, and educators to be well informed about the critical importance of an efficient vision system and how an inefficient vision system can destroy a bright child's future.

Jan Bratton, our Vision Therapy Patient Education Coordinator, perfectly summarized all the emotions involved when parents realize they have found the answer: "The relief parents feel when they are informed that there is something tangible holding their child back, and that there is treatment for the diagnosed problems, is an emotional time for them as well as for me. I know that in a matter of weeks after treatment starts, we will start to see some amazing progress, and life will be much more enjoyable for all concerned. I would like to make those feelings and realities available for everyone who has children who are not doing well in school or who work too hard at doing schoolwork. The joy of seeing them turn their lives around is incomparable."

Really, lives can change. Children having difficulty in school will start to function independently and more easily. Relationships with parents, teachers, and peers will improve; self-concepts will blossom. Homework will no longer take several hours or result in tears and frustration. Success in school, and subsequent lifetime milestones, will not be hindered by the defeat, sadness, failure, anger, confusion, loneliness, and rejection that accompany living with undiagnosed vision problems.

2 WHEN SOMETHING WAS WRONG WITH ME

11

2 WHEN SOMETHING WAS WRONG WITH ME

I can remember as early as second and third grade feeling behind the rest of the children in my class. Other children just picked things up faster than I did. When it came to spoken directions, listening, and especially reading, I was slow. Things always took a bit longer for me.

Later, in elementary school, I discovered something I was pretty good at. Math was easy for me: addition, subtraction, multiplication, and division. Having success with numbers, even being so young, gave me confidence and a little kick in my step. But to my great disappointment, that was not to last for long.

The numbers, when used alone, were easy to work with. But the moment word-problems were introduced, I bombed. This surprised me. It shook my confidence. I didn't understand how something that came so easy to me suddenly became almost impossible. I thought I could succeed, but the word problems with their foggy instructions and cloudy images created an obstacle that I could not hurdle. My wall of strength was gone, and I was the slow student again, still working on my quizzes and assignments while the other children went outside for recess.

In junior high, I resorted to other methods to gain popularity and acceptance. I was a fantastic class clown. Being funny and nonchalant allowed me to falsely feign the appearance of one who did not care. I was still okay; I could save face. After all, I was bright enough. I could get by, and I did. In fact, to this day, I clearly remember the title of the first book I ever read to completion. The Trouble with Jenny's Ear earned the honor of being my first successful read. I was so proud of myself! Even though I read my first book well after the other children in my class, I did it. However, reading it through was not easy. It took forever because I was slow, and it was not the least bit enjoyable for me.

Of course, my teachers observed my learning difficulties and shared this information with my parents at the bi-annual Parent Teacher Conferences. My concerned teachers, trying their best to help, suggested I visit the eye doctor. Consequently, the appointment with the eye doctor was not in vain. He prescribed glasses, which in turn, sharpened every image I saw. The leaves on trees, as well as the letters and numbers on the blackboard, were clear and perfect. But still, despite the glasses, I was a solid "D" student.

"Spirited" is how I like to label my behavior in my junior high years of school. My spirited inclination, combined with a bit of mischief, magnified my less than stellar grade point average. Fortunately for me, my parents decided I would move to Valley Forge Military Academy for my remaining high school career.

The environment was extremely disciplined. Every evening, for over two hours, the dorm rooms remained silent to provide an adequate atmosphere for concentration and study. The "no noise" policy was great for me! And because I worked slowly, this schedule provided plenty of time for me to complete my assignments. However, the extended period of locked down study time highlighted another problem. I was only able to focus for approximately fifteen to twenty minutes at a time. My eyes would become tired, and the words I read ran together.

Despite my slow pace and the necessary breaks I needed to get through, my grades improved to a strong "B" average. I knew I could do it. After all, I was a bright child, and I worked hard.

College was a similar scenario except that the setting wasn't quiet or disciplined. But I eventually learned to create that atmosphere for myself in the college library. Of course, that was after a first semester spent mostly at parties rather than at the library. After learning a lesson or two, I remembered what worked for me at Valley Forge, and I attempted to duplicate it.

I found myself requiring the same mental breaks about every fifteen or twenty minutes. My eyes and mind needed the rest. To insure my success in these larger lecture courses, I borrowed notes, compared them to my own and rewrote them, which activated my memory's recall. Of course, this routine involved a great deal of extra work, but I was determined. I knew I could be successful, and hard work and exhaustion would have to be part of my plan.

Just to be certain my eyes were not the cause of my learning differences, another visit to the eye doctor rewarded me with a stronger prescription for eyeglasses. Sharper eyesight was a blessing, but nevertheless, I could not read well.

Consequently, taking tests proved to be a difficult task. No matter how long I prepared for these assessments, deciphering the professor's questions puzzled me. I knew the information, but endured the same shaken confidence of the junior high school boy and test questions left me without an answer.

Not until my first year of graduate school did a young man anticipating graduation in optometry uncover the cause of so much frustration, disappointment, poor grades, and seemingly wasted time. This time around, the graduating optometrist performed a Functional Vision Exam. He discovered my vision problems. Soon after the discovery, I underwent Vision Therapy and my optometric Board Exams were, seemingly to me, the easiest series of tests that I had ever taken in my life.

I had been evaluated by talented and successful optometrists many times during my early life. Yet these vision difficulties remained hidden. Classical eye exams and eye health exams performed on me revealed only part of the problem, and these doctors treated only what they saw. However, the series of probing questions, the recognizing of symptoms by a trained eye, and other vision tests created to reveal these debilitating difficulties were never posed to me. My difficulties remained hidden because the disease's diagnosis remained hidden.

This truth about vision difficulties has existed for quite a while. But the overwhelming majority of optometric schools do not emphasize this education. As a result, when parents, teachers, tutors, pediatricians and other well meaning caretakers recognize a learning difficulty in a struggling student, and seek help, other more common diagnoses like dyslexia, Attention Deficit Disorder (ADD or ADHD), and now anxiety issues are in their forefront of awareness. This, combined with a lack of education about vision, creates circumstances where vision difficulties are often misdiagnosed.

Having gone through the educational system and barely survived, I have a special place in my heart for children who have these same challenges. Specifically, a decline in a child's self esteem, no matter what the cause, is a tragedy. But when this happens to bright children with vision difficulties, the deterioration in self-esteem is unnecessary.

It is a hard road for these students; I know it all too well. Making sense of the inability to perform like most of the others is painful. Self-doubt creeps in, relationships are strained, and other forms of coping rear their heads. Essentially, the child's future is compromised.

At least I finally knew what was wrong. No words can describe the relief I felt when I was diagnosed. Frankly, I was justified. Every bit of extra effort was explained. Every minute of recess lost was accounted for. Every poor grade was rationalized. My frustration was vindicated. My eyes played tricks on me and your child's eyes could be playing tricks on him, too.

Admittedly, I have been fortunate. People have helped me along the way, and I am grateful. I have also poured myself into hard work and have emerged successful. Now, I have dedicated my life to helping other children like me. If my staff and I can change lives positively, then I am totally fulfilling my life's calling.

3 How It Hurts: The Consequences of Learning-related Vision Problems

19

3 HOW IT HURTS: THE CONSEQUENCES OF LEARNING-RELATED VISION PROBLEMS

Having wrestled with the mentally, physically, emotionally, and socially exhausting consequences of my undiscovered and undiagnosed vision problems firsthand, I empathize with the pain and frustration you and your child might be enduring as you endeavor to uncover the source of the problem. You are not alone in this struggle. An astonishing 25% of children have some type of learning-related vision problem.   When added to the fact that for the first twelve years of life, nearly 80% of learning is accomplished through the eyes, the long term effects and classroom consequences become more and more apparent. Grades slide, teachers call, and the stress of trying to understand your despondent child builds.

Undiagnosed and untreated learning-related vision problems can wreak havoc on your family's happiness. Of course, this instability is understandable. For the parent, coping with the disappointment in your child's poor grades and apparent lack of motivation tests your patience. The new challenges of trying to help your child do better arise and add more frustration as your child is unable to catch on as quickly as you would like. Even worse, you see his countenance reflect a sadness and insecurity related to his frustration in the classroom. Seeing your child hurt for any reason can be unbearable for a parent.

In a child's life, untreated learning-related vision problems can rear their ugly consequences in the classroom, extra curricular activities, and even future career or lifestyle choices. Even more damaging is the effect of these untreated problems on the child's self esteem and his personal relationships.

Grades are merely numerical representations of a child's mastery in a particular subject. One would assume that early educational assessments, like the spelling test or the math quiz, should not have an eternal bearing on a child's future. Hopefully, the occasional poor grade would have little effect, if any, on the later years. But a consistent stream of below average results can ruin your very bright and capable child's chances of getting the encouragement and accolades he might deserve.

Without an impressive grade point average (GPA), your child's options for college or university education are reduced. His viable choices for a successful career can be limited, too. If his math grades are poor, then chances are he will not be studying to be an engineer or an accountant; if your child is resistant to studying due to discomfort and inefficiency, then applying for medical or law school is not probable.

Even outside of education, these undetected and untreated problems can have significant effects on your child's life. With an incomplete vision system, any multi-tasking at all will be a challenge.

The physically gifted athlete-in-training, who does not read as well as he should, will not have the sharp awareness that most superstar athletes possess. Phoenix Suns player Steve Nash's "no look pass" is keenly accurate because of his well-developed visual system. He sees the big picture. Likewise, a child with poor hand-eye coordination can swing the bat all afternoon only to make contact a few times. Other passions or talents, such as music or computer programming, can be inhibited by the presence of untreated vision problems as well.

Even more important than what our children do in the world is who our children are within themselves. Children build self-confidence from positive interaction between early childhood teachers, young friends, and their family. Beginning in elementary school, children take notice of who turns papers in first and who finishes the assignment last. We think of those years as the stress-free, carefree days of youth. But the reality for one who recognizes his slowness is one of self-doubt. They question: "What is wrong with me?" They feel stupid and think: "I can't do it." Obviously, the affects of this pattern of thinking are life changing.

With poor self-esteem, children do not like themselves. Then, they have difficulty liking others. Suddenly, bright children are different from the happy-go-lucky children on the playground. They might have trouble making friends because the weight of their shame is heavy and unattractive to others.

This shame carries over to the parent-child relationship, too. Children want to make their parents proud, but when insecurity takes over, they resort to isolation and even anger. The after school homework struggle is classic. Parents want to help; children cannot do it; parents do not understand; children feel defeated. No one wins.

Parents are often shocked when their children are clearly identified as having learning-related vision problems. They may experience guilt and ask themselves, "Why didn't I see this sooner?" My answer is a firm, "You never would have known." The subtleties only stand out to a trained eye or therapist. And from my own personal experience, I am keenly aware of the symptoms and situations where this type of learning difficulty can disguise itself as something more widely recognized in name.

Unfortunately, the news of good acuity or clear eyesight stops any further investigation into the visual system, and therefore, the more subtle vision disorders are often overlooked. Many times, these children can read the McDonald's menu, and they can hit the baseball with great accuracy. Why would anyone suspect the problem lies within the visual system?

4 WHY "20/20" VISION DOESN'T HELP

4

WHY "20/20" VISION DOESN'T HELP

"But wait, my child has perfect eyesight. She can't possibly be a candidate for Vision Therapy. Can this really help her?" You bet. One out of four children is faced with learning challenges due to an undiagnosed vision problem, even those with "20/20" eyesight. Undiagnosed. Undiscovered.

These undiagnosed vision problems remain so for two reasons. One reason is that there is no eyesight problem. The child has "perfect vision" or "20/20", and therefore, has no reason to visit an eye doctor. Or, possibly the child has visited an eye doctor and has walked out of the door smiling with a clean bill of eye health. The well-educated eye doctor saw no need for corrective lenses. No glasses or contact lenses were prescribed for this child. Secondly, this undiagnosed vision problem was overlooked because the suspected eyesight problem is corrected with contact lenses or glasses. Only part of the problem is solved.

What is commonly known as "perfect vision" or "20/20 vision" is a measure of visual acuity. It is a measure of how clearly we can see. This function is mostly determined by reading letters on a chart from a twenty-foot distance, otherwise known as The Snellen Chart.

Most of us can easily see the giant "E", and most of us become increasingly nervous, as the letters get smaller. Because younger children typically cannot identify the alphabet, some eye doctors use another chart. The letter "E" pointing to the left, the right, up, and down replaces the series of letters on the adult version of the Snellen Chart.

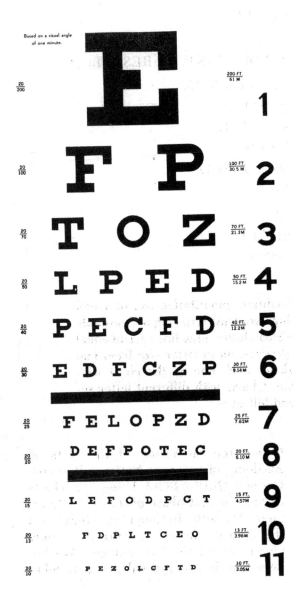

However, some others need corrective eyewear to improve their eyesight or to sharpen their visual acuity. A child needs the ability to see small objects from a distance: the Matchbox car on the floor, the letters and numbers on the chalkboard, the baseball hurling through the sky, the minute musical notes on her sheet of piano music, the hundreds of words on his book report book page, or even the stars in the night sky. Your child's visual acuity needs to be sharp to be successful in today's world.

At the 1999 Parent Teacher Association National Convention, the following resolution regarding the relationship between vision and learning was adopted. Interestingly, they also recognize the problems that arise when "typical" or traditional vision screenings fail to identify other types of learning-related vision problems.

LEARNING-RELATED VISION PROBLEMS EDUCATION AND EVALUATION

Whereas,   It is estimated that more than 10 million children (ages 0 to 10 suffer from vision problems; and

Whereas,   Many visual skills are necessary for successful leaning in the modern classroom; and skill deficiencies may contribute to poor academic performance; and

Whereas,   Typical "vision" evaluations/screenings only test for a few of the necessary learning-related visual skills (distance acuity, i.e.20/20 eyesight, stereo vision, and muscle balance), leaving most visual skill deficiencies undiagnosed; and

Whereas,   Learning-related vision problems, when accurately diagnosed, can be treated successfully and permanently; and

Whereas,   Knowledge regarding the relationship between poorly developed visual skills and poor academic performance is not widely held among students, parents, teachers, administrators and public health officials; now therefore be it

Resolved,   **That National PTA, through its constituent organizations, provide information to educate members, educators, administrators, public health officials and the public at large about learning-related visual problems and the need for more comprehensive visual skill tests in school vision screening programs performed by qualified and trained personnel; and be it further**

Resolved,   **That National PTA, through its constituent organizations, urge schools to include in their vision screening problems tests for learning-related visual skills necessary for tests in the classroom.**

Ironically, having "20/20" eyesight has little to do with having "perfect vision." Vision is much more than measuring how clearly you can see. It is a complex process that involves over twenty visual abilities and more than 65% of all of the pathways to the brain. Nearly 80% of what a child perceives, understands, and remembers is dependent on a properly functioning vision system.

Sight refers to what we see. Vision is the ability to understand what we see. Sight is a natural ability, and vision is a learned process. Both can be improved.

5 WHAT A CLASSIC EYE EXAM CAN FIX

31

5 WHAT A CLASSIC EYE EXAM CAN FIX

There is no doubt that a good fitting pair of eyeglasses can revolutionize the life we lead. The millions who have experienced transforming clarity through corrective lenses know exactly what I mean. I have heard observations directly from patients, and assuredly, parents have heard words of excitement and amazement from their children as strands of hair and leaves on trees come into focus. Eye care professionals are trained to help change lives.

They welcome us into their offices, and as we get comfortable, we are asked to iterate random letters on eye charts with our alternate eyes open. The clicking noises are mesmerizing and mysterious, signaling the doctor's attempt to find the perfect corrective lens for his patient.

These thoughts often go through the minds of my patients: Exactly what is my doctor doing? "Is it better here? Or here?" As my chin rests on the tissue-covered ledge, what is my doctor able to see when he peers through the microscope?

This chapter attempts to take a bit of the mystery out of the typical eye examination. And more importantly, with your new education, you will be prepared to get the best out of your next exam and so will your child.

A "classic" eye exam begins with a comprehensive history of the patient's eyes. The doctor might ask, "Why are you here? How can we help?" Starting off on the "same page" is critical. In my experience, two of the most common reasons for making an appointment are lack of sharpness or clarity (acuity) and eye discomfort or fatigue after visual tasks. For whatever reason we seek out the help of our optometrists or ophthalmologists, it is crucial for that reason to be known by both parties involved.

Once the doctor gathers the basic facts, eye health becomes the doctor's primary focus. You will be asked to look to the left and to the right, up and down, and in a circle. We check your "ocular motility" with a pen-light. This means we check how easily you can move your eyes in all directions without moving your head. What is the condition of the muscles that control your eye movements? Do your eye muscles work in the way they should? We judge how well the muscles inside your eye are working by asking you to read from a card held sixteen inches from your face.

Next, the doctor assesses pupil reflexes, again with a pen-light. We look for appropriate reactions to the stream of light and also note the reaction of the opposite eye as the light is directed elsewhere. From there, the exam transitions to the interior and posterior areas of the eye.

Once your chin is resting comfortably in the designated chin rest and your forehead is leaning forward against its own rest, we use the biomicroscope to detect anomalies (defects) in the following parts of the eye:

- the cornea,

- the iris - the colored area of the eye,

- the sclera - the white part of the eye,

- the conjunctiva - a clear membrane that covers the entire surface of the eye, and

- the pupil margin.

In addition to being able to see what is happening within your eye, we are also able to check for signs of systemic diseases, such as diabetes, hypertension, elevated cholesterol and even multiple sclerosis.

Often, patients wonder exactly what their eye doctor is able to see by looking through my biomicroscope at the tiers of your eye. Your cornea is an amazing 0.5mm in thickness and consists of five separate layers. In order from front to back are the corneal epithelium, Bowman's membrane, the stroma, Descemet's membrane, and finally the endothelium.

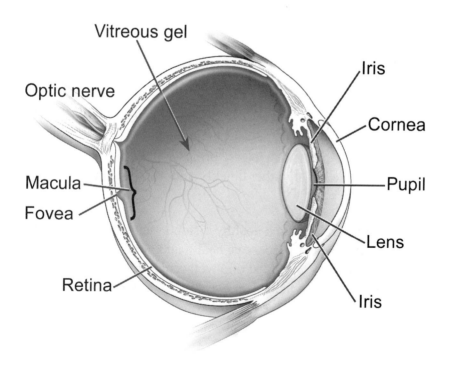

The crystalline lens is located behind the iris. The function of the lens is to help the eye to focus by getting thicker or thinner. It works similar to an auto-focus camera. With age, this lens becomes less flexible or even rigid. This phenomenon is often recognized by people in their forties as the need for reading glasses increases.

The posterior or back half of the eye is made up of the vitreous body, which is a clear gel like fluid similar to egg whites, and the retina with the optic nerve head. Here, your eye doctor can detect any signs of glaucoma and optic nerve degeneration. Additionally, a swollen nerve head caused by an increased cerebrospinal fluid pressure might suggest the presence of a tumor.

Another point of interest is the macula. The macula is a geographic location on the retina consisting of a high concentration of photoreceptor cells and nerves. The fovea is the central point on the macula containing the highest concentration of photoreceptor cells. Macular degeneration, a more common anomaly today, occurs when the macula becomes unhealthy. Macula tissue breaks down for many reasons: the affects of long-term cigarette smoking, extended ultraviolet light exposure, or even a lack of the necessary dietary intake of essential vitamins and minerals.

These intricate components that, together, make up the eye as an organ each play significant roles in comprehensive eye health. In the classic eye exam, an eye care professional can accomplish an assessment of eye health rather quickly. Indeed, this is all part of the "Standard of Care."

Eye health is critical to a healthy vision system. As mentioned in the previous chapter, proper eye health and good eyesight are only two items on the checklist of a well functioning vision system. Although there is more than clear eyesight to proper vision, checking acuity and eye health by an eye care professional are the first steps to becoming confident children are able to see as well as they should.

MYOPIA

The most common diagnosis for fuzzy vision is myopia, more commonly known as "nearsightedness." People with myopia see better at near distances, such as when reading a book, than at far distances, such as driving a car. Children with myopia may squint at the blackboard, but have no problem at all seeing their toys or parents' faces.

Myopia occurs for two primary reasons: a GENETIC predisposition and ENVIRONMENTAL causes. Many children experience progressively poorer far eyesight from age eight through adulthood, and. often, one or more parents or grandparents have demonstrated this same pattern. Some research suggests that over exertion of the eyes is not the primary cause because many of these individuals have not demonstrated a pattern of excessive reading or computer use in their lifetimes.

Most eye doctors typically prescribe full correction eyeglasses that should be worn at all times for progressively poorer far eyesight. However, some more effective strategies can be used to minimize the progression of the nearsightedness. These can include purposefully under-correcting distance acuity to 20/25 or 20/30, wearing bifocal glasses, and/or completing a program of vision therapy.

Many children who experience blurry far vision do so primarily as a consequence of the substantial amount of "nearpoint" activity such as playing computer games, watching television, reading, and other doing deskwork activities associated with school. Their vision systems may not be developed enough to handle the stress and strain associated with many of the aforementioned activities.

A landmark study performed in the town of Barrow, Alaska, a community whose culture relies on the fishing and whaling industry for their very existence strongly supports the environmentally induced theory of myopia. In this town, only a few citizens had blurry distance eyesight.

In 1949, when Alaska became a state, all the children of Barrow were required to attend public school for the very first time. There they spent many hours indoors and doing deskwork, and were only able to look as far away as the size of the small school buildings that housed them. At night, they read by candlelight. They no longer spent the majority of their day outdoors using their eyesight to see at far distances. By 1950, the incidence of myopia had increased significantly in the school age children from this community.

Our children have many wonderful opportunities to accelerated learning during the preschool and early education years of their lives. Along with those opportunities, they spend longer hours with "nearpoint" vision types of work like practicing letter writing, coloring, cutting, and doing lessons in their workbooks. These activities put potential strain on young and developing vision systems. A complete functional and developmental vision evaluation by a developmental optometrist can determine if children's vision systems are well enough developed to do these tasks.

The entire process of vision both derives meaning from and directs action to our environment. Some visual demands may be too strenuous or too complex for children's vision skill levels. Kids will try their best to meet visual demands and are initially excited about the new skills they are learning. When the task places unnecessary strain and confusion on the vision system, children become frustrated if unable to be successful. As a result, they make incorrect adaptations, and develop inefficient and harmful habits that can further damage or distort an otherwise normal vision system.

This phenomenon is seen when children try to copy the letters of the alphabet before they have the ability to discriminate the subtle differences between similar letter shapes.

Hyperopia and Astigmatism

Other common eyesight problems are astigmatism and hyperopia. In astigmatism, the cornea or the lens of the eye is more oblong shaped than it should be. The result is blurry and strained eyesight. Hyperopia is the opposite of myopia. Hyperopia is defined as the ability to seeing objects in the distance clearly. Astigmatism and hyperopia can be also be corrected with lenses or laser surgery.

Eyeglasses

Even though this book's purpose is to shed light on the often-misunderstood relationship between eyesight and vision, the important role of glasses, contact lenses, and laser surgery cannot be ignored. The terms glasses, eyeglasses or spectacles can be used interchangeably and denote the combination of both a frame or eyewear and lenses, which are usually prescribed by a doctor. Prescription lenses can be used for three different purposes: compensation, stress reduction and performance training.

Compensatory Eyeglasses

First, the most common type of lens is COMPENSATORY. Compensatory lenses correct a patient's nearsightedness, farsightedness, or astigmatism.

Compensatory glasses allow the patient to enjoy his best-corrected eyesight. A person's best-corrected eyesight can be better than, less than or measured right at 20/20 visual acuity.

These prescription lenses are not really correcting vision; instead, they are merely compensating for the error within the eye that is responsible for the lack of clarity. Because the patient's eyesight is unclear or blurry again when the glasses are removed, their eyesight is obviously not "corrected."

STRESS RELIEVING EYEGLASSES

STRESS RELIEVING lenses allow the vision system to function at a more optimal level of efficiency. These lenses absorb the unwanted visual stress and strain so that the eyes can relax. For example: A nearsighted child may be prescribed lenses that purposefully leave them with best-corrected eyesight of 20/25 at distance, even though a prescription lens that allows them to see 20/20 does exist. Prescribing a less than full distance correction allows the child to not only see well at distance but clearly and comfortably at near or at 16 inches.

Bifocal lenses are another common way of using stress-relieving lenses. These lenses are prescribed when a child needs two sets of lenses to see well at different distances. One particular prescribed lens might be appropriate for seeing far, and at the same time, this lens might be too strong and impede the child's ability to see near. While some families choose for their child to wear two separate pairs of glasses for different situations, bifocals are another alternative.

Ironically, many children who are prescribed stress relieving or performance lenses, as they are sometimes referred to, have the gift of 20/20 visual acuity in each eye without the aid of glasses. But, the examination demonstrated that prescription lenses, specifically measured for this child, substantially enhanced the visual performance of his vision system.

Children should wear stress-reducing lenses for any near point activity at school or at home, like reading or doing homework; we refer to these as "indoor glasses." Stress relieving lenses have two benefits. First, they provide greater comfort and efficiency for reading, writing and computer activities. Second, they reduce straining thus allowing children to retain their gift of excellent distance visual acuity.

PERFORMANCE TRAINING EYEGLASSES

PERFORMANCE TRAINING lenses can be used in conjunction with a vision therapy treatment program prescribed by a doctor, and directed by a vision therapist. Used in this fashion, lenses and prisms act as powerful tools for neuromuscular training and re-training of components of the vision system.

6 WHAT'S GOING WRONG: INTERFERENCE WITH THE MIRACLE OF VISION

43

6 WHAT'S GOING WRONG: INTERFERENCE WITH THE MIRACLE OF VISION

"The whole is greater than the sum of its parts." Whether or not this well-known phrase is valid in all areas, it is certainly true with vision. While the Snellen Eye Chart measures eyesight and visual acuity by assessing the distance at which our eyes see clearly, the Snellen Chart does not and cannot give a complete representation of how the eye works as a whole. After all, seeing the chalkboard clearly is only half the picture.

However, vision is more than just seeing clearly. While our eyes' ability to focus is critical, if acuity is in check and our retinas are working properly, other vital visual processes, which occur in the blink of an eye, are also essential to evaluate.

The eye is also the GATHERER of INFORMATION. When the eye is healthy, it is able to gather the best information. Sharp acuity and healthy eyes are the first part of a properly functioning vision system. The eyes gather information by scanning a page, focusing on a blackboard, studying a painting, glancing at the television screen, watching the game, or looking at any one of millions of objects. Two major functions of a healthy information gathering system are its binocularity and saccadic fixation.

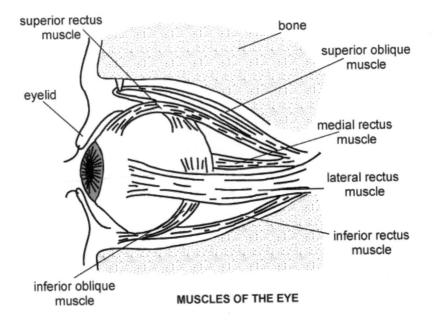

superior rectus muscle

bone

superior oblique muscle

eyelid

medial rectus muscle

lateral rectus muscle

inferior rectus muscle

inferior oblique muscle

MUSCLES OF THE EYE

Binocularity refers to the eye's ability to point in the proper direction. The alignment of the eye is achieved by controlling six muscles. With each eye properly aligned, the two eyes together produce a fused picture. Each eye sees a different image, and successful vision happens when the two eyes' separate images fuse together correctly.

When the eyes team and aim together normally, print on the page is simple and clear

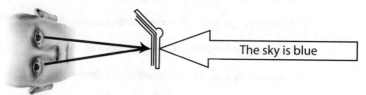

The sky is blue

Reading requires the eyes to aim in together at the same point on this page. Vision is clear, single, and comfortable as long as both eyes are aiming at the same point.

When eye teaming breaks down, the eyes aim independantly and print doubles

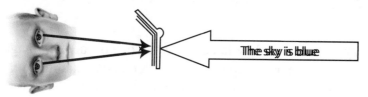

The sky is blue

Children with eye teaming problems find it difficult to maintain the inward eye aim required for reading. As the eyes tire, they move in or out and end up pointing at different places on the page. The result is blurred or double print.

When our eyes are looking at a book twelve inches from our face, our eyes turn in or converge. Likewise, when our eyes look up from the book to peer across the room at an object far in the distance, our eyes turn out or diverge. When our eyes are not properly aligned, our brain sees the two separate images each eye produces. The result of this single malfunction: double vision or diplopia, can be devastating to the child in elementary school or the teenager trying to succeed in high school.

There once was a little girl who could not read very well. She complained that the print was blurry and moving. She could not keep her place on the page. She went to her optometrist to get help. Her optometrist recommended vision therapy and told the girl that there was a solution to her vision problems. The girl began vision therapy and saw drastic improvements in her reading, writing, and most off all how she saw the world. The vision therapy made a huge difference in her life!

"Lazy eye" or Amblyopia occurs when one of the two images is blurry, even with prescription glasses. A clinical examination identifies any pathological or structural reason for the reduced vision in one eye. A patient may have a lazy eye that points straight ahead or one that turns inward or outward. "Functional amblyopia" or lazy eye is clinically defined as a difference in best-corrected acuity between the right and left eyes of two lines or more on the Snellen acuity chart.

An exaggerated version of eye misalignment is commonly known as cross-eyed or wall eyed, or a "strabismus". This visual condition is easy to spot, and is sometimes incorrectly referred to as lazy eye. Fortunately, because this vision difference is often obvious to a parent or teacher, an optometrist can recognize and treat it early, and limit further consequences.

However, a slight misalignment or mild strabismus, is more difficult to identify, and may not even be visible to the naked eye. Although insignificant in appearance, these so-called minor misalignments can have serious negative consequences on vision and motor development, and can cause undue frustration in the classroom and beyond.

Children, who have a strabismus, see a fused picture. They register the two images, one from each eye, but instead of the two images blending perfectly into one, as they should, either a blurred image or two partial images imposed over each other result. Without knowing that their vision is flawed, children who have a strabismus see differently than everyone else.

Typically, problems of this nature become more evident in elementary school with tasks such as copying from the board, as the eyes and brainwork hard to focus and make sense of competing images with little success. Symptoms of living with misaligned eyes are frequent rubbing or squinting in hopes that refocusing will fix the problem. Stress and tension from obvious eyestrain could also result in headaches.

A person's two eyes must work together as a team to retrieve information and send it to the brain quickly and efficiently. For reading such as this, the eyes successfully move across each word and line and, intuitively, discern the exact point on the page at which to begin the new line of text. These eye movements are called saccades. Assuming your eyes have smooth saccadic fixation, you do not lose your place, or skip lines as you read.

Athletes in training must use both eyes to watch a ball. Athletes who miss the ball may have eyes that individually follow the arc and path of the ball, but do not blend the two separate images of the ball's pathway together into one. This visual difference results in the athlete missing the ball because the brain does not receive accurate information and misjudges the ball's location even though the eyes see it clearly.

Children who suffer from eye teaming or focusing dysfunction are often unaware that they are not reading exactly what is on the page or seeing exactly what is physically present. They may thus get little meaning from the paragraph they have just read, or they miss the ball. If aware of their vision difference, they might improve their reading by using a finger as a place marker. Athletes, sometimes compensate by closing an eye. These compensatory techniques work, but result in slow and unsure comprehension and athletic skills and declining confidence.

After the eyes GATHER INFORMATION from what they see, the brain must PROCESS the INFORMATION into vision. From the eye, the information travels along the optic nerve through several processing centers including the visual cortex. Here, the brain analyzes the data received and assigns meaning to it.

While reading, the brain might ignore punctuation, reverse letters, and jumble words together. A "d" might be read as a "b," or a "p" as a "q". Hand – eye coordination occurs when the brain translates the data into meaning and creates reality. A child with a visual motor integration problem will struggle with the act of writing the answer to the test question on the page. His eyes, brain, and hands do not cooperate to reach the desired outcome. But, this child knows the answer, despite what the blank test page suggests.

Neither reading nor writing is reliable. Spelling is also poor because the brain writes something different than what a child wants it to. Visualization allows the brain to create an image in motion in the "mind's eye" even before it is completed. Students with visualization problems may know the answer to the test question, but have difficulty writing a response on paper. The three integral functions of vision, gathering, processing, and visualization should all meld together at this point, but they do not.

We refer to the "Five F's" as the necessary visual components that together create this miracle of good vision.

THE "FIVE F'S" ARE:

1) Fixation
2) Following
3) Focus
4) Fusion
5) Form perception

The gathering of information by the eyes, the processing of that data by the brain, and the visualization of the image into meaning are all separate systems that, when working properly, are interwoven to create the miracle of good vision. This happens in the blink of an eye. Each component should be instantaneous.

Children with well-developed vision systems can handle more complex environmental demands by, unknowingly, multitasking in a calm, efficient and effective way. Children with undeveloped vision systems will struggle to perform any one or more of these "Five F's."

Here are some examples of what it often looks like for children with vision system problems involving the "Five F's."

How Well Could You Read if Print Looked Like This?

These are representations of what it might look like if you had a Learning-Related Vision Problem. .

> There once was a little girl who could not read very well. She complained that the print was blurry and moving. She could not keep her place on the page. She went to her optometrist to get help. Her optometrist recommended vision therapy and told the girl that there was a solution to her vision problems. The girl began vision therapy and saw drastic improvements in her reading, writing, and most of all how she saw the world. The vision therapy made a huge difference in her life!

> There once was a little girl who could not read very well. She complained that the print was blurry and moving. She could not keep her place on the page. She went to her optometrist to get help. Her optometrist recommended vision therapy and told the girl that there was a solution to her vision problems. The girl began vision therapy and saw drastic improvements in her reading, writing, and most of all how she saw the world. The vision therapy made a huge difference in her life!

> There once was a little girl who could not read very well. She complained that the print was blurry and moving. She could not keep her place on the page. She went to her optometrist to get help. Her optometrist recommended vision therapy and told the girl that there was a solution to her vision problems. The girl began vision therapy and saw drastic improvements in her reading, writing, and most off all how she saw the world. The vision therapy made a huge difference in her life!

> Thereoncewasalittlegirlwhocouldnotreadverywell. Shecomplainedthattheprintwasblurryandmoving. Shecouldnotkeepherplaceonthepage.Shewentto heroptometristtogethelp.Heroptometristrecommen dedvisiontherapyandtoldthegirlthattherewasa solutiontohervisionproblems.Thegirlbeganvision therapyand sawdrasticimprovementsinherreading, writing,andmostofallhowshesawtheworld.The visiontherapymadeahugedifferenceinherlife!

For more information, contact:
Toni Bristol, COVD Spokesperson and Media Contact
media@covd.org

Dr. Stephen Miller, Executive Director
College of Optometrists in Vision Development, St. Louis, Missouri
(314) 991-4007 or smillod@sbcglobal.net

Fixation refers to the saccadic fixation movements. Our eyes fixate on one set of information at a time. In early stages of vision development, eyes can only fixate on a small amount of information – a few letters or symbols. As the vision system matures, children are able to expand of the reach of fixation and jump to the next segment with amazing agility.

For example, in a one-line sentence, the more mature eyes might "jump" once or even twice, while the underdeveloped eyes might require six or more "jumps" to absorb the information in the line. Amazingly, optometrists have standardized the number of saccadic movements appropriate for each grade-level. The eye movements can be measured and using an infrared "jump" or movement detector.

Following refers to the action of return sweep our eyes perform as we reach the end of a line on a page. The eyes' automatically locate the next starting point and proceed with the next line. Following also refers to the speed and the sequential manner in which our eyes move.

Focus describes the clarity with which the eyes see an image: clear, blurry, or even clear in one eye and blurry in the other. Two common focusing difficulties are accommodative infacility and accommodative fatigue. Those with accommodative infacility find it difficult to shift from looking at near to looking far away. This problem occurs when children read a book at their desk and then look across the room at a chalkboard or overhead projection and find the print to be blurry. Focusing fatigue occurs when children have difficulty keeping the printed words held at a 16" distance clear and comfortable for even a short period of time. Children who can "see like an eagle" on the weekend, yet complain they can't see the board in school, often have accommodative problems.

When children have trouble focusing on text in a book it may look something like this:

There once was a little girl who could not read very
well. She complained that the print was blurry and
moving. She could not keep her place on the page.
She went to her optometrist to get help. Her
optometrist recommended vision therapy and told the
girl that there was a solution to her vision problems.
The girl began vision therapy and saw drastic
improvements in her reading, writing, and most of all
how she saw the world. The vision therapy made a
huge difference in her life!

Fusion is eye teaming. Eyes team together to gather images. If the image is close, then eyes converge or turn in so that both eyes can equally absorb the information. As the object is pulled farther out, the eyes straighten their line of vision. Extreme cases of convergence insufficiency can cause strabismus.

Lastly, form perception incorporates the skills and abilities involved with perceiving information. Perceptual skills include identification, discrimination, spatial awareness, and visual sensory integration. These visual cognitive skills are used to process visual information to the brain to be organized and interpreted.

Problems in only one of the above areas can be detrimental to a student's performance in the classroom. Because all parts create a healthy whole, one slight variation in a normally functioning system can initialize a domino effect of frustration. The solution begins with recognizing the symptoms as visual, not educational or psychological. An assessment and evaluation by a trained professional, a developmental optometrist, who can readily identify vision problems is critical. The sooner these problems are detected, the easier they are to fix. However, it is never too late.

7 WHERE ATTENTION DEFICIT DISORDER (ADD) AND DYSLEXIA FIT IN

55

7 WHERE ATTENTION DEFICIT DISORDER (ADD) AND DYSLEXIA FIT IN

Symptoms of both Attention Deficit Disorder and Attention Deficit Hyperactivity Disorder can often be the same or similar to symptoms of visual disorders. Many times, children diagnosed with ADD or ADHD are really suffering from something altogether different and totally treatable with Vision Therapy.

In a previous chapter, I mentioned the multi-faceted visual processing and integration system, which is responsible for your vision after the health and functioning of the eye itself checks out okay. Tasks like eye teaming, eye tracking, and perception can easily malfunction and produce erroneous visual images.

When this occurs, a child may see double. Or he might even omit words or lines, or, to him, letters can even seem to be reversed. In actuality, there is an internal struggle going on within his vision system, and the child isn't even aware of it! There is no standard for him to compare his struggle with, and consequently he is frustrated, exhausted, and not least of all, he cannot see what is truly there.

What does the resulting behavior look like to his teacher? Certainly, you can imagine that the child is restless after a few minutes of strain and concentration. And with a short attention span, he might begin to daydream or doodle and maybe even possess a poor attitude. Regardless of his physical behavior, the child will begin to fall behind and lose interest in his classwork. Of course, his grades will suffer, and the teacher will notice.

So clearly, it is easy to confuse common vision disorders with Dyslexia or with the diagnosed and sometimes medically treated ADD or ADHD. With the acceleration in academic standards for younger children and the impact of a poorly developed vision system, it is not surprising that many of these diagnoses are missing the mark.

For the sake of the child's future, the true cause of his frustration must be uncovered. A misdiagnosis can postpone healing and reclaiming his normal, stress free, academically achieving, athletically successful, socially acceptable, and family friendly life.

Another component to address in appropriately diagnosing these children is their visual system. Just as in visual processing related problems, these patients with the other diagnoses like ADD, ADHD, and even Dyslexia have "20/20" vision. This usually sidetracks the patient, the patient's family, and the school counselor from considering visually related problems.

I can understand why it is often assumed by the schoolteachers and counselors, after eyesight is checked and measured at "20/20," that the most probable cause for these problems is dyslexia. The child's work frequently contains reversed letters. His reading comprehension is poor, and he is embarrassed to read aloud.

A dyslexia diagnosis is not always a correct assumption. In fact, after a series of Vision Therapy sessions, these "dyslexic" symptoms frequently disappear.

Also easy to confuse are untreated visual disorders with recognizable behaviors associated with ADD or ADHD. Children might appear uninterested in class lessons and begin to be disruptive when it is simply the result of the child's struggle with reading. Restlessness and frustration are key symptoms of a poorly developed vision system because these children cannot process every-day information like their peers.

There are many symptoms common to children with learning-related vision problems and children with ADD/ ADHD. Extra-active physical traits like moving around and having trouble playing quietly are unique to the behavioral disorders. Learning-related vision problems surround the insufficient vision system and can always be traced back to that one function. A developmental vision evaluation by a developmental optometrist will be able to reveal the truth.

SYMPTOMS OF AD(H)D:
ATTENTION-DEFICIT/HYPERACTIVITY DISORDER[1]
Compared to Symptoms of a Vision Disorder

Symptoms	ADHD (DSM-IV*)	Learning-Related Vision Problems	Normal Child Under 7
Inattention (*At least 6 necessary*):			
Often fails to give close attention to details or makes careless mistakes	X	X	
Often has difficulty sustaining attention in tasks or play activities	X	X	X
Often does not listen when spoken to directly	X	X	
Often does not follow through on instructions or fails to finish work	X	X	X
Often has difficulty organizing tasks and activities	X	X	X
Often avoids, dislikes or is reluctant to engage in tasks requiring sustained mental effort	X	X	X
Often loses things	X	X	X
Often distracted by extraneous stimuli	X	X	X
Often forgetful in daily activities	X	X	
Hyperactivity and Impulsivity (*At least 6 necessary*):			
Often fidgets with hands or feet or squirms in seat	X	X	X
Often has difficulty remaining seated when required to do so	X	X	X
Often runs or climbs excessively	X		X
Often has difficulty playing quietly	X		
Often "on the go"	X		X
Often talks excessively	X	X	
Often blurts out answers to questions before they have been completed	X	X	
Often has difficulty awaiting turn	X	X	X
Often interrupts or intrudes on others	X	X	X

[1]Chart: © Copyright 2000-2006 All Rights Reserved Patricia S. Lemer, M.Ed., Executive Director, Developmental Delay Resources (DDR) 800-497-0944 www.devdelay.org

* DSM-IV: Diagnostic and Statistical Manual of Mental Disorders, 4th Edition

This chart is courtesy of Educational consultant, Patricia S. Lemer, M.S. Bus., N.C.C., M. Ed., who founded the Developmental Delay Resources which is an excellent resource for parents of special needs children. www.devdelay.org.

There are many possibilities to consider when disruptive behavior presents itself. Nutrition is one major factor contributing to a child's behavior. Colored dyes, too much sugar, and allergic reactions can all play a significant role. A doctor, pediatrician, or nutritionist can suggest alternative diets to rectify the negative behavior.

> *Vision Therapy can make a world of difference.*

The behavior can also be the result of emotional distress experienced at home or at school or even in the neighborhood. In this case, a psychologist or school counselor would be a wealth of information and assistance for you and your child.

An occupational therapist can aid in reteaching physical skills like crawling for those children with sensory integration problems that manifest themselves in behavioral disruptions. There is research indicating that developmental milestones are key in setting pathways for normal learning skills. Reteaching those missed milestones restructures the pathways and might allow for more peaceful behavior.

And of course, disruptive behavior might result when a child's close work (reading or writing) is too uncomfortable to bear. He doesn't know he is having difficulty seeing properly but experiences frustration and failure instead. So, it makes sense that he would react negatively. In this case, Vision Therapy can make a world of difference.

Parents are usually left out of the loop because they defer questions of their child's performance to teachers who see them daily. Teachers are a reliable, qualified source for evaluating how children are doing in class and in their social circles. Every day, teachers work directly with our children. They see how our children interact with others, and observe them as individuals. Truly, teachers are the experts when it comes to our children's education.

And because teachers are with our children every day for seven hours, we should appreciate their instincts. But, parents, you also know your children. It is important that you make an educated decision regarding what to do with your struggling child. What does that mean? You should gather information and be aware of your family's options before you make a final decision. Your child's future depends on it.

Vision related problems are often dismissed because the schools' health system screens students for eyesight clarity using the Snellen Chart. When eyesight measures "20/20" or even slightly less, vision is usually automatically ignored as a possible cause for the problems in class.

Every single year, thousands of children slip through the system with undetected vision problems only to be suspected of something such as ADD/ADHD or even dyslexia soon after. Considering the detrimental effects of untreated visual problems, poor self esteem, missed opportunities, strained relationships, and harmful grade averages, my goal is to uncover the hidden truth and help these children before more damage is done to their lives.

With an increasing frequency of ADD or ADHD diagnoses made each year, more and more children are taking Ritalin, Adderall, Concerta or other similar drugs. Many say the drug helps with focus or attention span, but many others say the drug has adverse effects, as well. In addition, research has shown that the medication does not improve the ability to read and learn.

According to the results of a study published in the August 2003 issue of Journal of Family Practice: "Although psychostimulants showed a short-term decrease in symptoms in students diagnosed with predominantly inattentive ADHD, they did not significantly improve grade-point averages." An article in the July 2005 Scientific American also stated, "Studies increasingly show that while medication may calm a child's behavior, it does not improve grades, peer relationships or defiant behavior over the long term."

An article from the "Annals of Family Medicine" written by Leonard Sax MD, PhD and Kathleen J. Kautz, RN, BSN states, " The amount of methylphenidate (eg, Ritalin, Concerta) prescribed in the United States increased by more than 55% between 1991 and 1999, while the prescribing of amphetamines (eg, Dexedrine, Adderall) increased by more than 2000% during the same interval." An article from the "Annals of Family Medicine" written by Leonard Sax MD, PhD and Kathleen J. Kautz, RN, BSN states, " The amount of methylphenidate (eg, Ritalin, Concerta) prescribed in the United States increased by more than 55% between 1991 and 1999, while the prescribing of amphetamines (eg, Dexedrine, Adderall) increased by more than 2000% during the same interval."   Compared to the rest of the world's nations combined, the United States consumes five times more Ritalin.

As we discussed in the previous chapter, the symptoms of ADD and ADHD and the symptoms of learning-related vision problems can manifest themselves in the same way. Among other causes, nutritional deficiencies and sensory integration issues can also be the root cause of "ADD and ADHD type behavior." But knowing those alarming statistics, discovering the true problem is critical.

So what is it that the teachers are observing in their classrooms that would suggest ADD or ADHD? Teachers see children that aren't quite ready to perform to the level that is requested of them. Of course, some follow instructions with ease, and consequently, great success. But some children are just resistant to failure. Instead of failing time and time again, they turn away from the task at hand and inevitably get into trouble.

You may have overheard some parents say, "My daughter's teacher is just not trying hard enough." Lack of teacher effort is not the reason for this phenomenon. Today's children are very different from those children of yesterday. Over the past thirty years, our children play outside less, daydream less, run less, and even have less time to think. Think about it: television, computers, reduced outdoor play, and earlier academic demand have replaced the body's natural image creating processes. Their minds are just busy doing other things!

The good news is that once the underlying vision problem is corrected, the child is then able to respond more rapidly to other forms of remediation, such as tutoring, special services available through school, occupational therapy, etc. In many cases, the bright child who used to be smart in everything but school often excels once the visual roadblock is removed.

8 What a Child Needs for Success in Pre-K

8

WHAT A CHILD NEEDS FOR SUCCESS IN PRE-K

Children must have a certain level of both visual perceptual and motor development to be successful in the early grades: nursery, kindergarten and first grade. An innate developmental hierarchy provides children with the skills and abilities to be successful when written language is presented to them and they are asked to identify, interpret and respond to written symbols. Many of our children are asked to read, write, and spell before they have the skills or tools to do the job effectively.

Motor development refers to the ability to control the body's movements. Visual perceptual development refers to the mind's ability to interpret and integrate information that is taken in visually. Vision is essential to both developmental systems: How high should I lift my arm? How high is two feet? Where is the pencil and paper? Where would you like me to write my name? Where is the cup? How deeply do I place the spoon inside the cup to retrieve pudding?

Toddlers illustrate the perfect example of not being able to create visual images. Those two year olds touch everything. They even want to taste everything. Toddlers gain knowledge by developing the ability to create images by assigning value to those images by figuring it out on their own. Visually competent children actually think in pictures, even when only words and language are used.

These Visually competent children will experience better success with letters, sounds, phonics, reading, and simple math because they will automatically imagine a visual memory with each of the lessons. For example, when you read the word "cat," your mind instantaneously assigns meaning to it because you recall the image. You do not, however, recall the definition of "cat."

As children become more and more visually competent and assign picture-like images to words, they will be the most advantageously ready for written language. A word must mean something before it can be connected to the written word. Parents, this is why reading to our children is of the utmost importance. This time allows for their fresh imaginations to stretch with detail and meaning.

Unfortunately, many of the early educational environments encourage letter and number recognition, and some encourage reading, well before the vision system is ready for such learning.

So, why do so many children in the United States of America have such a difficult time learning to read? Understanding how we use our eyes when reading may give more clarification. Our eyes first recognize the shapes of the letters and assign sounds that we need to hear. Together, these sounds create words. These words, in turn, represent images, and from those images, we create meaning. Really, our language is comprised of at least five steps.

In other countries, language, reading and comprehension are not the same. Amazingly, there are NO incidences of dyslexia in China. Chinese languages, comprised of symbols, do not rely on phonics at all. Chinese school-aged children do not learn to read until much later when they are neurologically ready. For them, reading is all about vision.

In a study conducted on eye movement behavior in toddlers in Oslo, Norway, researchers found that when babies younger than 32 months eye an object, they hold the object with their eyes until it is in their hands, and with their hands, fingers, and mouth, they continue to discover the object without using their vision. But after 32 months of age, the toddlers continue to hold it with their eyes while their hands and fingers explore the object. At this age, the toddlers are becoming more adept at binocular vision. Researchers realize that a child's vision system is not fully developed until the child reaches approximately eight years of age.

As a result of this study, Scandinavian countries do not introduce reading instruction until children reach the third or fourth grade. Even more impressive, these countries' reading scores have shot to the top of the comparative lists by the time these children reach the seventh grade.

Commonalities of successful readers include excellent imagery skills, minimal muttering or whispering while reading (subvocalization), more whole word recognition, and fewer saccades. Remember, saccadic movements are the jumps from one grouping of words and letters to the next in a line of text. With this information, it is evident that forced early reading will only prevent successful reading instead of encourage it.

What happens when an inappropriate task is asked of children, before they are developmentally ready? The children avoid the task but are repeatedly asked or encouraged to reattempt it. Since they cannot do it correctly yet, they repeatedly perform the task incorrectly. This behavior is learned, memorized, and embedded in children's memory and is difficult to change.

Parents sometimes wonder if their children are ready for Pre-K or Kindergarten, and, if not, what steps to take to help them become more prepared. One red flag is if one or both parents had learning problems growing up, there is a good chance that these undiagnosed learning-related vision problems could have been passed on to the child. Vision problems often run in families.

The condition of the child's coordination and balance can also be an indicator. Referring back to the hierarchy of development, if the child has poor gross motor development (learned to ride a bike or a skateboard "late"), then chances are the other developmental milestones will be later, too. In addition to gross motor, poor fine motor development is also an indicator. Drawing, painting, and making symbols are examples of fine motor skills.

Even pregnancy health, like whether or not the mother smoked or was around secondhand smoke and her quality of nutrition, can impact the perceptual motor development of the child. Consider the conditions of the child's birth or delivery. Were there any complications such as the necessary use of forceps, a breech birth, a premature birth, or low birth weight?

And finally, children's right and left directional abilities can be indicators. By age seven to nine, most children have the ability to project direction within them. For example, they might be able to explain to you where they are in the room: "left of the coffee table and right of Fluffy's bone."

By no means is the above information a checklist for school readiness. But, my hope is that parents are aware of the hierarchy of development. There is an order in which our bodies are programmed to learn tasks, and as parents, we need to foster patience and love and lay the foundation for good learning. Pay attention to your child's habits, especially work habits. And if you can recognize avoidance or any discomfort, seek attention quickly so the faulty patterns do not become embedded into your child's memory.

9 WHAT VISION THERAPY IS AND HOW IT CAN HELP

9 What Vision Therapy is and How it can Help

Vision Therapy, also called Vision Training, can be described as physical therapy for the vision system. In a Physical Therapy session, patients perform "exercises" and physical activities with various muscles and parts of the body that have been injured, are causing discomfort or have restricted performance in some way. Physical therapy treatments condition muscles and restore movement and usage to these particular malfunctioning areas of the body. Patients are actually training or retraining that part of the body to function correctly. Vision therapy works in much this same way.

The primary difference between physical therapy and vision therapy lies within their focus of the different treatments. Interestingly, the focus of vision therapy is NOT to strengthen eye muscles. Our eye muscles are already one hundred times stronger than need be just to simply move our eyes. Instead of strengthening exercises, vision therapy is a form of physical therapy for the eyes and the brain. The eyes are a physical extension of the brain. We certainly look with our eyes, but we "see" with our brain; vision therapy retrains our eyes and brain to receive, process, and interpret information the way in which the system was intended.

Vision is an extremely complex process that may be likened to a sophisticated computer system. Most of us have experienced the frustration of sitting in front of a computer, expecting it to work properly, and not being able to complete our desired task because of some sort of "computer malfunction". The malfunction can be anywhere: the hardware or equipment, the connections and wiring, or the software. The malfunction may be with the physical components of the computer or the 'hardware' involved. It may be a result of an operating program malfunction or a 'software' problem. In either instance the desired result is to solve the problem so we can effectively complete our desired task.

So it is with the eyes. The typical eye examination determines if the eyes and other parts of the vision system are healthy and determine if the 'hardware' is in good working order. When the 'software' is the culprit, finding the exact source of the malfunction often requires assessing the function of many different processes and how they interrelate to one another. 'Software' problems often require an optometrist who has specific training in visual development, a Developmental Optometrist, to determine the exact nature of the problem along with the best treatment options, which often includes Vision Therapy. Vision Therapy is incredibly effective at resolving vision malfunctions especially within the "software" of the vision system.

The physical health and structure of the eyes could be considered to be the hardware. When the eyes are healthy, vision "hardware" issues are usually improved with eyeglasses or other corrective lenses. Many people have efficiently working vision systems, but need the assistance of corrective lenses for clearer eyesight. Others, however, have "20/20" eyesight but have a "software" dysfunction making reading and/or sports difficult. These people do not need or benefit from prescription eyeglasses.

Instead, they need vision training or vision therapy to retrain their eyes and brain to work together to relay the incoming messages appropriately. Vision therapy does not strengthen eye muscles, but it is extremely effective in the treatment of physiological, neuromuscular and perceptual malfunctions of the vision system.

We value clear eyesight, but vision is much more than seeing clearly. Vision is the process of deriving meaning from what we see and then it directs our actions to get our desired result. The determination of the medical necessity of optometric vision therapy comes from an extensive analysis and subsequent diagnosis of how the vision system is functioning. Scheduling an appointment with a developmental optometrist and undergoing an evaluation will be the first steps to take.

Vision therapy is an individually customized and supervised treatment program that also varies according to the individual doctor's postdoctoral education. In our office our vision therapy program is designed to correct visual-motor, perceptual and cognitive deficiencies (that are the result of visual deficits). The courses of therapy will vary according to the diagnosis made and the severity of the situation. Each treatment program is created especially for the patient on an individual basis.

Depending on the depth of the problem, treatment can vary from stress relieving or performance lenses (see Chapter 5) and/or anywhere from sixteen to eighty hours of in-office therapy.

It is important to know that a vision therapy program truly is a commitment for the family and the person for which the program has been designed. This is because home exercises will be assigned in addition to the in-office treatment. Typically, these home treatments are fun and enjoyable, but they are indeed challenging and essential for optimum success in the program. As those home exercises are repeated and practiced more and more, the patient will note improvement in his vision at a quicker pace.

These therapy exercises are methodically re-teaching the eyes and the brain to perform differently than they have been. With consistent effort and reliable practice, these pathways of performance will become automatic. This is why home treatments are essential to the program. It is beneficial for the parents or caregivers to be participants with the patient in the program. They can offer support, encouragement, coaching, and an eye for detail when reinforcing technique really matters.

Optometric vision care professionals supervise vision therapy and many types of specialized and/or medical equipment are used in Vision Therapy programs. Comprised of much more than eye exercises, a course of vision therapy treatment might include the use of some or all of the following professional tools: prescription lenses (regulated medical devices); therapeutic lenses (regulated medical devices); prisms (regulated medical devices); optical filters; occluders; electronic targets with timing mechanisms; computer software; vestibular (balance) equipment.

When symptoms of learning related vision problems are detected, most parents stop at nothing to find a solution to ease the pain surrounding all of the natural consequences involved. Before vision therapy is considered, parents have often already invested in some type of special education assistance in the classroom, extra tutoring or educational programs at a local learning center, physicians, or psychostimulant medication. When these options don't result in improvement, the peace of mind that would come as a result of solving this problem is worth every dime.

Practically speaking, the cost of an entire individualized vision therapy course of treatment will depend on the severity of the problem and the course of treatment prescribed by the doctor, but can be as much as braces (orthodontic treatment). The College of Optometrists in Vision and Development (COVD), outlines specific guidelines for appropriate doctors, insurance companies, and patients and answers many questions pertaining to treatment. Some insurance companies do participate in payment for vision therapy and services; many do not. But whether or not payment assistance is offered does not reduce the need for receiving treatment. No value can be placed on a properly functioning vision system.

While the results of vision therapy are permanent, the ever-changing visual demands of today's world can sometimes create new problems. The good news is that should this occur, treatment is often very short. Vision therapy is extremely effective at eliminating visual system problems that interfere with a child's ability to learn and perform to their potential.

10 How Michael Found His Strengths

10 How Michael Found His Strengths

Like many little boys, Michael has always loved computers and trains. He has a special talent with computers, too. However, a special interest in trains may have been the only connection Michael had with other boys his age.

In the third grade at his community school, Michael attended special education classes; he needed the extra attention in many areas. He hated to read, and his handwriting and spelling skills were poor. In addition to those somewhat normal symptoms of typical, growing children (especially boys), Michael had difficulty organizing his time and his activities. Loud noises bothered him, and this aggravated his hyperactivity.

Michael's response to noises and distraction was not normal. His problem with focusing in class was so disabling that teachers would often find him under his desk. It was hard for Michael to make friends and feel part of his class community. Consequently, Michael's self confidence and social skills were below normal.

After consulting with medical doctors, psychiatrists, and psychologists, to no avail, his parents visited us for a last attempt to do something for their child. Just as his parents described, we noticed the same types of behavior when Michael was initially examined and evaluated.

As we observed Michael playing with kindergarten building blocks, it was evident that his eyes did not maintain contact with the blocks. They jumped from place to place never resting for long. We observed an introverted little boy. Even in the office, Michael displayed poor motor skills and disruptive behavior. Beneath all of the outward distractions that Michael was accustomed to using, it was clear to me that he was an intelligent child. He just didn't know how to direct his efforts and act accordingly.

> *We knew his life would be in for a dramatic change.*

Following a successful program of Vision Therapy, Michael started fifth grade. We knew his life would be in for a dramatic change. Michael's grades improved dramatically as his ability to focus increased. I am also pleased to note that Michael began to make and keep friends, and his relationship with his parents was more about loving communication rather than frustration. His mother remembered: "There was a big difference after vision therapy, both for him, and for us. It actually changed who he was."

Michael now loves to read. Reading is actually one of his favorite subjects, and the proof lies in the improvement of his grades. He has even moved from special education to mainstream classes. In the afternoon, after school, he breezes through his homework and class assignments like he has never missed a beat.

A letter from Michael's vision therapist summarizes his experience:

When Michael started therapy, he could focus on a task between one and two seconds. His motor development, fine and gross, was so underdeveloped. Through hard work, Michael's achievement was astounding!

He was able to function marvelously in the regular classroom. No more special programs for Michael. All of his grades soared, especially in the language arts and math areas.

Michael went to school with a new confidence. His teachers found the change "hard to believe". He was a different child! He was outgoing, self-confident, interested in athletics, and he had friends to play with.

After Michael's final session, Michael said to me as he was going out the door, "Mrs. Anderson, I'm not an idiot anymore."

Claudette Anderson
Vision Therapist

As demonstrated in my own story, vision disorders can take away and destroy the most human of behaviors. Now, after vision therapy, Michael relates to his peers more positively, and likewise, they can relate to him.

You can imagine that Michael's self esteem soared with his new friends and success in school. Instead of an introverted, misunderstood, underperforming child, Michael's muscle balance and coordination improved to match other boys in his current grade level. For the first time, Michael even tried out for a couple of athletic teams.

Each day, Michael's parents marvel at Michael's post vision therapy successes. They are ecstatic about their son's happiness and are relieved that there was an answer for him.

11

HOW KAREN REGAINED HER INDEPENDENCE

11

HOW KAREN REGAINED HER INDEPENDENCE

Before I tell you about Karen, we need to make one point very clear. This book is written for parents of children that are looking for the answer to the ever-present question in their lives. "What can I do to make my child's learning experience more effective?" I feel that I have the answer. But, it is never too late to change a situation. And it is never too late to make a difference in your own life. Vision Therapy benefits children entering the second grade, wandering pre-teens beginning high school, young adults embarking on a college or graduate education, and the adult who has always known that something wasn't right.

Your vision system is structured in a way that, no matter your age, certain techniques can improve and even restructure your vision in a few months. With just a small amount of time and effort, you can finally resolve the issues that have been plaguing your own vision, and subsequently, your own learning for decades. With that said, I'd like for you to meet Karen.

Karen, a woman in her mid 40s, nearly died and suffered from severe brain injuries as the result of an automobile accident. Her injuries caused her to have double vision, blurred vision, and she had difficulty with depth perception. She recalls standing at the top of an escalator filled with fear and trepidation as she hesitated to take the first step onto the moving staircase to descend. She could not see the steps form and therefore was unable to form a clear picture in her brain of how far she would have to step down before her foot rested safely on the metal stair.

Of course there were many impediments that Karen encountered each day. Walking simple distances required a tremendous amount of concentration. She could not walk without watching her feet or needing something or someone to hold on to. Karen considered the constant survey of her feet to be a gentle reminder to her brain that her feet were actually walking on solid ground. She was receiving an incorrect visual message from her vision system and needed to reassure herself that she would not fall. She encountered the same difficulty stepping off curbs. Her lack of depth perception was sending the incorrect message to her brain, which in turn was throwing off her perception and processing.

Her brain injuries also prevented Karen from driving because she could no longer multi task. Steering, braking, glancing in the rearview mirror are all fluid motions for some but for Karen, driving proved to be impossible. Being only 45, a life without the freedoms driving provides was not an option.

Sadly, on a visit to a local defensive driving program, Karen was told that she was nowhere near ready to be behind the wheel. She shared with the instructors that she had previously completed months of physical therapy and had been told that there was nothing else they could do for her. The driving school suggested she make an appointment to see me and discuss the possibility of Vision Therapy as a solution to her problems. Karen made the appointment to see me, was evaluated, and her success story began.

As I evaluated Karen, her answers to my patient questionnaire provided more insight into what she was experiencing: she could not read; her thought processes were often unorganized; her peripheral vision and depth perception were markedly poor; and concentration was sporadic. In addition to all of these obstacles in her life, Karen was homebound unless someone took her out.

The program I suggested for Karen included four intensive months of Vision and Processing Therapy. Of course the therapy involved hard work, but Karen was more willing to sacrifice time and effort to gain the results I had promised her.

After her first appointments, Karen habitually walked out of our office and across the parking lot to her friend who was waiting to drive her home. Four-inch steps and a staff member helping her step off the curb marked that short walk. These small steps and extra help were a constant reminder that she was no better.

The turning point for Karen was about ten weeks into the program when she walked down the step and straight across the lot without an ounce of hesitation and no assistance. She relates, "I did it without any problems, and I continued to improve from there. I could do the normal things in life again!" That accomplishment was a huge breakthrough for her and certainly one she will never forget.

Life did get better for Karen. Not only were steps and curbs a non-issue, but she retook and passed her driving test. She no longer needs assistance; she comes and goes by herself. Karen is independent once more. Her eyes are teaming which has eliminated her blurry and double vision. In addition, we have recorded a significant expansion of her peripheral vision as well as her depth perception.

Karen will tell you that vision therapy has changed her life. She says, "Vision therapy has been a godsend for me! I don't know what I would have done without this program. Thanks to Dr. Spinozzi's Vision Therapy program, I think I am one who can truly be called a survivor."

12
How Nic "Recovered" from ADD

12

How Nic "Recovered" from ADD

Since Nic was in the first grade, his teachers had noted his reluctance to read. Individual reading plans had been suggested because he was so far behind the rest of his class. Up through the fifth grade, Nic was reading two to three years behind his expected levels. Running out of possible solutions, Nic was tested and diagnosed with Attention Deficit Disorder or ADD.

His parents, however, knew ADD was not the cause of his reading problems. ADD suggests that paying attention to any one thing for an extended amount of time would present difficulty. Contrary to this unfocused behavior, Nic loved constructing models, something that required time, attention to detail, concentration, and perseverance. Perhaps it really wasn't his lack of concentration that was at fault. Perhaps Nic's problems were caused by something else.

Of course in other ways Nic reflected characteristics of the typical child with ADD. He hated to read, and he read slowly. In some cases, occasionally he did show signs of having a short attention span. Homework took an abnormally long time to complete. Organizing his thoughts and memorizing material was a struggle. He was frequently frustrated with school, assignments and, consequently, himself.

Fortunately, Nic's parents brought him in for a routine eye exam to see if he was a candidate for corrective eyeglasses. His mother explained her son's experience with schoolwork, so I suggested Nic come in for a Vision Therapy evaluation. During the screening, the symptoms mentioned previously were evident. In addition, other symptoms typical of a vision problem were present. Nic skipped lines when he read; he repeated words and lines; and, his writing was crooked and poorly spaced.

Having exhausted other resources, Nic's parents decided to research Vision Therapy and its benefits. Nic's mom consulted with the family's pediatrician and left confused because the physician was skeptical of the program's claims. The doctor concluded that Nic's problems were due to a poorly trained teacher or, even more probable, Nic was just not working hard enough. Still, those conclusions did not resonate with Nic's parents. Surely, something else was amiss.

Investigating further, Nic's mom discussed the Vision Therapy with his fifth grade teacher and the school's vice principal. The vice principal, having witnessed other children's successes with vision therapy, was very encouraging. Nic's fifth grade teacher was supportive at the attempt to find the true cause and solution to Nic's problems. Each of these educators wanted him to find success and was willing to help in any way they could.

Having completed their research, Nic's parents were now more confident than ever that Nic's problems had been properly diagnosed and that Vision Therapy was the answer. Nic started vision therapy. At first, Nic and his parents had to plan ahead and make sure they were allowing time for the home therapy assignments. Finding the time was understandably difficult as there are many other things a fifth grader likes to do. Family time is critical, and finding those moments in the midst of a weekday is tough, especially when fifth graders already have their school homework to complete. A few weeks into the program when they saw Nic's improvement, all of the extra effort was more than worth it.

As they observed Nic's progress and accomplishments, his parents were ecstatic. His mother comments, "The results were incredible! By the end of Nic's fifth grade year, he was reading above a sixth grade level. He was tested more than once, so we know it is true." Nic's confidence skyrocketed, too. His mother shared a comment he made to her one afternoon. He said, "I'm not dumb. I CAN read, and I CAN write." At this point, Nic's parents and teachers were noticing daily breakthroughs and important triumphs that became consistent.

After the completion of the vision therapy program, our office recorded these changes in Nic's performance: His grades in school improved markedly. He completed his homework in half the time it previously took. His eyes were no longer tired after reading. He accepted new assignments and challenges without hesitation. His spelling and handwriting improved greatly. He developed an interest in reading that did not exist before therapy. He reads more often even without encouragement.

His parents feel a great sense of relief at how well Nic is doing. And they are surprised at how much he has changed. With just a few short months of hard work and effort and without ADD medication, Nic is capable of succeeding.

13 HOW JOSH JOINED IN

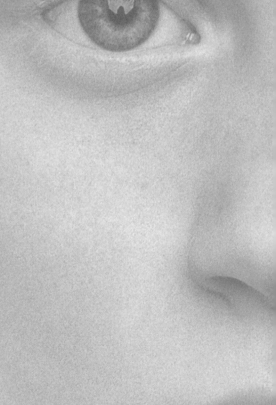

13 How Josh Joined In

Before Vision Therapy, those responsible at Josh's school decided that Ritalin was the best solution for his struggles. He was quickly diagnosed with ADHD (Attention Deficit Hyperactivity Disorder), and medication was prescribed. Even though Josh's parents trusted the physicians and school authorities with their son's well being, they both acknowledged that Josh did not display many of ADHD's typical symptoms.

In fact, Josh, age 8, never acted out of line. He showed no signs of hyperactivity; he certainly was no class clown. Josh was a well-behaved, compliant child with academically related issues. However, his short attention span took its toll on Josh's classroom performance. He was unable to focus on the task at hand, he seemed totally uninterested in classroom activities, he had difficulty copying from the chalkboard, and his handwriting was poor.

Josh says he felt like an "outsider" because he couldn't keep up with his peers. He had few friends, and he didn't feel good about himself. Because he couldn't "get it," he even thought he was "dumb." At home, things weren't much better. Josh did not get along with his step siblings very well because he wasn't coordinated enough to play many sports, something they all loved to do.

Josh knew he was different. If there was a new task at hand, he would often cry and give up if it presented even a slight challenge. His parents enrolled Josh in several tutoring programs and LD or Learning Disabled classes in hopes that some improvement would be seen or some skills gained that would translate into finding friends and community that he could be happy about.

Like many of my other patients, Josh's family found their way into my office. I observed that Josh closed one eye when he read, and his eyes tired quickly which resulted in a "burning sensation" after a short period of reading.

Looking further into Josh's vision and processing system, we discovered that Josh had a severe case of both blurred and double vision. I explained that Vision Therapy would help Josh a great deal.

Later, after Josh completed the program, his mother was quick to say that the Vision Therapy program was quite a commitment in time and effort, but "Josh loved all of it. Even when I was tired after a long day, Josh would remind me, "Mom, I've got to do my stuff for therapy!""

For Josh's family, Vision Therapy was the answer they had been looking for all along. Prior to Vision Therapy, homework time was a disaster. Josh's mom says, "The hours of homework were endless, and one of us would always end up in tears. Now Josh likes doing homework, and he even picks harder books to read for fun."

As a result of the therapy, Josh's confidence soared. Soon after the program was completed, his reading and math scores increased. He has even jumped several reading levels. Josh now has new learning skills, and he says that these are helping him feel that he can accomplish his schoolwork. His mother recounts that, "Now Josh doesn't have to struggle to see what the other children were automatically seeing."

Vision Therapy proved to be a family builder, too. Josh's body coordination improved so much that he is now able to play sports with his stepsiblings. His newly developed binocular skills are responsible for the coordination and confidence that is necessary to make these activities possible for him.

Overall, Josh's entire interaction with people has changed. With his new confidence and academic success, Josh can relate to children in his class much easier. The lack of physical coordination that kept him from being an active member of his family is no longer an issue. He joins in as a contributing family member. His much improved self esteem allows him to hold his head up high and look others in the eye when he speaks to them. All of this success was accomplished with no medication at all!

14
HOW CONNOR BECAME CONFIDENT

14
HOW CONNOR BECAME CONFIDENT

Connor's mom says: Vision therapy has been, by far, one of the best things we have done for our son. For many years, he complained about blurry vision and not being able to see the board in school. We have taken him to have his eyes examined only to be told that his vision was fine and that he may have weak eye muscles, and ultimately, years down the road, he would need glasses for distant vision.

Although we knew our child was smart and had the ability to do well, school was a struggle. He hated school, homework, and would never read on his own although he enjoyed having books read to him. Hours and hours were spent doing homework with me by his side telling him to focus. "Just apply yourself," I would say. At times, it was a nightmare.

Then one day, I received a flyer from Dr. Spinozzi's office with a short article about Vision Therapy. The article had several questions asking about symptoms, which might indicate a vision problem. I could answer yes to all of the questions. Since my son was complaining yet again about his sight, and in fact, was writing his homework incorrectly every night, I made an appointment with Dr. Spinozzi.

Finally, I found a doctor who would get to the bottom of why a child, who was otherwise quite capable, was just not performing like we expected him to or thought he might. As it turned out, Connor was diagnosed with a vision problem that countless other eye care professionals missed, dismissed, or knew nothing about.

We started vision therapy immediately as we were facing relocation. What a blessing and true miracle Vision Therapy has been. I was a bit skeptical but willing to try. After only three weeks, we noticed a great improvement not only with his vision but also in his confidence and self-esteem.

Connor was thrilled when he noticed how much better he was at playing basketball. His penmanship improved greatly. He felt sure of himself. For once, he believed that he was smart and capable. It was a mother's delight to see all of the hard work pay off when Connor, for the very first time and without any encouragement, picked up a book to read for pleasure.

After only four short weeks my child, who was barely getting C's in math, went from a low "C" to an "A." We were in the midst of a very big move, and Vision Therapy seemed like just one more thing to add to our very full plate. However, we made the time and our son's vision a priority, and what a huge payoff we received in return.

Since then, I have shared Dr. Spinozzi's pamphlets with past teachers that our son had hoping they will recognize the same symptoms in future students and be able to direct parents like myself in the right direction. Thank you, Dr. Spinozzi, for finally helping us to discover what was "wrong" with our son. Who knew that vision was more than good eyesight?

The staff at Eyecare Specialties is the best, and I would unconditionally recommend Vision Therapy to anyone. The results will speak for themselves. Don't wait.

Connor's case is not unique or extraordinary. He was a seemingly typical middle school student that avoided schoolwork and was often distracted in class. He had difficulty copying from the chalkboard or overhead projector, which made "paying attention" in class even more of a struggle.

From those descriptions, you can understand why his teachers didn't quickly assume there was something wrong with Connor. Many assume that children who fit the above description are typical adolescents avoiding work and being lazy with the quality of the work they choose to do. However, his parents recognized a discrepancy in Connor's school performance and his behavior, attitude, attention, and interest when he wasn't there.

When Connor came to our office for an initial evaluation, we noticed more specific difficulties, which Connor didn't even recognize in his own struggle. He reversed letters and numbers; he skipped lines when he read; he misaligned digits in columns; and to him, print went in and out of focus. His case wasn't unique at all. In fact, it was a classic case of Convergence Insufficiency: a common learning-related vision problem.

After therapy, Connor performed in school just like we expected him to perform. His reading comprehension improved; his handwriting became more uniform and neat; his math scores improved because he properly aligned his numbers and did not reverse them.

In turn, Connor was a happier child. In the afternoons, homework was a much more pleasant process and quicker to complete. That eliminated so much of the parent-child relationship stress and allowed home to be more of the comforting and welcoming place it should be. When a child experiences such success in school and receives lauds and accolades from teachers and parents, it is not surprising that parents and those close to the child see a significant difference in the child's demeanor.

On the athletic field, because Connor didn't miss as many balls and was quicker on the field, he found similar lauds and accolades, which came from coaches and peers. Connor was less clumsy and more outgoing, ready for anything and willing to try. Really, for children, that's what it's all about, right? Now, his future is wide open, and Connor is no longer limited to what he can achieve.

The "trickle down effect" of vision therapy can be life changing for the child. He is more able to realize his full potential, and he knows it. Changes such as these can take place within a few months, and therefore the differences can be seen within the same school year and even the same semester. Of course, this is a great pleasure to observe as a parent, full of relief and amazement. And it just happens to be one of my favorite perks of the job.

15
HOW JON SUCCEEDED AT SCHOOL

15
How Jon Succeeded at School

"Before our son, Jon, had his first appointment with Dr. Spinozzi, he was two grade levels below average in reading. He was in a special reading class at school because he was considered to have learning disabilities. He had his eyes checked several times by our regular eye doctor who told us Jon had "20/20" vision with no problems at all.

When he started having headaches in class, we decided to take him to Dr. Spinozzi to see if he could determine the cause of the headaches. He found that Jon had "convergence dysfunction" or, rather, Jon was seeing double. No wonder he couldn't read and he was having headaches!

We immediately started Jon in the Visual Training program, and five months later, Jon is now reading at his grade level and no longer needs that special reading class. Most importantly, Jon's confidence and self-esteem have improved tremendously, and he loves going to school. He even reads for fun, not just because he has to read for school. We're thrilled with the progress! This is the best thing we've ever done for Jon."

Jon, a regular, ten year old boy in the fourth grade was almost like the other children. The only irregular thing about him was he hated school. There are many young children who don't love the confining routine of the school day, but for Jon, it was different.

The stress and discomfort of school brought him to tears almost every day when he came home. As a parent, you can imagine how heartbreaking those afternoons might be.

Jon would complain about his math classes in the mornings and his difficulties with reading; the painful headaches only compounded the problem. Following their instincts, Jon's parents brought him to their family optometrist, but his eye doctor's accurate diagnosis of Jon's "20/20" vision only hid the true cause of Jon's frustration and unhappiness.

Jon's situation exemplifies the common misunderstanding and misinformation that inevitably postpone a true diagnosis of learning-related vision problems. Most adults observing Jon's troubles would assume he needed glasses or even a remediate level math and reading class, but with a "20/20" vision diagnosis, corrective lenses and vision problems are typically ruled out as possible causes for struggles such as his.

Yet in Jon's case, his vision was the cause of it all. His double vision made reading almost impossible and working math problems was an uncomfortable and unreliable process. Consequently, Jon did not understand why this was happening. Wasn't he like all the others? Jon's frustration and confusion were directly causing his poor self-esteem. The combination of failure in school and lack of self-esteem, in turn, made it more difficult to make good friends and be accepted by the other children in his class. Who would want to go school with a situation like that?

As a father and a doctor, it breaks my heart to see children experiencing life like this, and all so needlessly. I was one of these children; I know what it is like. This is why we are so pleased with Jon's results after he completed a vision therapy program.

In just a short amount of time, Jon's special education reading teacher told his mother that she noticed a huge improvement. His test scores increased in the following increments: 20/100, 50/100, and 60/100, to a 70/100. His most recent test scores in math went from a 13% to a 58%. In reading, his most recent scores went from a 30% to a 90%. Jon is now reading on his grade level, the 4th grade.

Jon once thought he was the "dumbest child in class." But now he sees himself as "one of them (the others) and pretty smart, too." His parents say that vision therapy is the best thing that has happened to Jon and the best money they've ever spent. Their son's life is proof enough.

16

HOW LAUREN IS EMBRACING CHANGE

16 How Lauren Is Embracing Change

Lauren was considered to be a good student: she finished all of her work and always gave it her best effort. Her good grades reflected the eleven year old's determination and consistent hard work despite having undiscovered learning-related vision problems. Her parents recognized the unusually long time it took for Lauren to complete her homework or other school assignments, but they did not consider the unnamed difficulty to be severe or debilitating.

At the beginning of Lauren's fifth grade year, her teacher observed Lauren's difficulties with reading. Not only did was Lauren's reading fluency poor, but there was a significant lack of interest in any kind of reading at all.

Lauren's teacher was well-versed in the common symptoms of learning-related vision problems because her own son was diagnosed with some vision difficulties shortly before this time. The teacher's son had recently completed a series of Vision Therapy and was keenly aware and able to spot the sometimes camouflaged conditions.

117

Armed with experience and a hunch, the teacher performed a quick eye-tracking test on Lauren, and with what was observed she recommended that Lauren's parents make an appointment for Lauren to be evaluated as soon as possible. Fortunately, she did.

Now, unlike the other children described in this book, Lauren has not yet finished her therapy regime. She is only eleven sessions into her series of therapy; for Lauren's case, this is approximately one third of the way complete. However, it is for that reason Lauren's situation is included in my book.

In such a short time and with only a few months of therapy, Lauren's parents and Lauren's teacher can already see a significant improvement in her performance in class, on homework, and socially, too. Her reading fluency has increased; her confidence has increased; and routine homework doesn't take nearly as long as it once did. It has been reported that in the last few weeks, Lauren's demeanor is "much more bubbly" and she seems happier.

Her vision therapist has noted a definite change in her willingness to be at her therapy sessions. This makes a significant difference because her eagerness to be present in the session will enhance the therapy's result. In turn, Lauren has had an increased desire to practice her prescribed techniques at home. All of this stems from her own recognition of the changes and improvement she has experienced, and only one third of Lauren's vision therapy is finished.

Lauren's initial screening at our office showed her to be experiencing a severe case of double vision. Ironically, Lauren never suspected it. Rarely do children recognize the problem. You have to remember that children who suffer from learning-related vision problems have nothing with which to compare their poor vision. Children readily adapt to their circumstances and accept the faulty vision as normal when it is truly debilitating.

Instead, they might complain of discomfort when they read, or they might attempt to describe words moving on a page, or they might say they lose their place easily when reading. None of these complaints would alarm a parent or teacher enough for them to seek attention as soon as possible. And even more unfortunate is none of these complaints even hint at the magnitude of harm that these difficulties can do to a child.

Teachers, you are the child's advocate here. Just like Lauren's teacher recognized something more from observing her in the class, you can be the one to help change the lives of those in trouble, even more than you already do. Lauren was "a good student." Imagine the possibilities that await her after her vision therapy is completed.

17 How to Test Your Child at Home

121

6. Imagine what would happen if the other coin was uncovered. Would four pennies appear? Try it.

7. Do you see four coins? Continue to focus on the pencil and move it closer to your eyes.

8. Stop when three coins appear and attempt to discover what different eye movements do to the appearance of the three coins.

9. Are the three coins level? Is the center coin clear? Is the pencil point clear? How many points do you see? You have moved it too far if you see more than one pencil point. Practice focusing on the one point.

10. By moving the point toward Lincoln's nose on the coin, try to make the penny "float" as if suspended in air.

Mastering each step of this exercise is important, and an inability to perform one portion of the exercise indicates a heavier reliance on one vision capability over the other. More than likely, some of these steps will be easier to master than others. But regardless of your success, this is an interesting exercise to do with your eyes.

BROCK STRING TEST

For this exercise, you will need a shoelace or something similar. In the middle of the shoelace, place a paperclip or piece of tape.

1. Hold the ends of the shoelace in each of your hands.

2. Place one end of the shoelace at the tip of your nose.

3. With the other end, extend your arm to its full reach so that there is a line of shoelace spanning from your nose to your other hand.

4. Adjust the paperclip to be approximately mid-way from your nose to your hand.

5. With both eyes open, focus on the paperclip in the middle.

6. How many strings do you see from your nose to the paperclip? How many strings do you see from the paperclip to your farthest hand?

When we look at something, the image we see is a result of the relationship between the two eyes. This exercise should prove to you that each eye works independently of the other, but properly functioning vision is the blending and cooperative effort of both eyes together. This is simply one way to check if both eyes are working together comfortably.

Upon looking at the shoelace, you should see two strings instead of just the one you know is truly there. You should no longer see only one string. If both of your eyes are focused on the paperclip, then the shoelace will diverge from that point to your hand and become an image of two strings going in separate directions. In addition, the same will apply to the section of string from the paperclip to your nose. Likewise, the string will appear to converge (or go to) the paperclip from separate directions. This is because each eye is seeing the shoelace differently.

Ideally, your eyes should see "both strings" with the same brightness and crispness. However, if one eye is stronger than the other or if one eye is working harder than the other then you will see only one of the images. You will see the strongest eye's image. In some cases, you might see both images but one would be dimmer than the other.

Also, check to see where your two strings cross. Do they cross at the paperclip junction? If they seem to cross before or after the paperclip, this could indicate a binocular vision problem.

This exercise indicates the complexity of the vision system. Many things work together to provide the image we "see," but there is a lack of education about the processes that occur after the visual information has been absorbed by the eye's lens. Simply trying these at home will give you a better feel for how complex the visual system is and perhaps bring an awareness of learning-related vision problems to light.

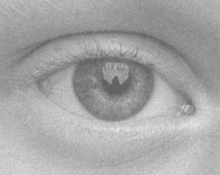

18

HOW WE KNOW THAT VISION THERAPY WORKS

129

18
HOW WE KNOW THAT VISION THERAPY WORKS

Here in our Parker, Colorado, office, my therapists and I have been "blown away" by the changes we see in our patients' lives. We are witnesses to the dramatic differences in their before-and-after life situations, and we know beyond a shadow of doubt that the results are life altering.

To prove my point, I included specific and detailed cases of these success stories in the testimonies from Karen, Josh, Michael, Nic, Connor, and Lauren. Each of them now has an opportunity to have a better life than they would have otherwise. Doors are now opened to them after their commitment to Vision Therapy that were closed before. The increase in their confidence alone is amazing to behold – and all from doing eye exercises!

As each new patient comes to the office for their initial consultation, my staff, of course, asks them to fill out a series of paperwork. The first form they are asked to fill out is the "Pre-screening Questionnaire" on which are listed a series of symptoms. The patient, along with their guardian, checks off the symptoms that apply to them like: headaches after reading or skips words or lines when reading.

Later, after eight to ten weeks of therapy, the patient fills out a similar form called the "Vision Therapy Achievement Report" which is then compared to the original Pre-screening Questionnaire filled out at the initial consultation appointment. I know, paperwork is not the most thrilling part of the process, but for us, it provides an invaluable tool for measuring the otherwise unbelievable before therapy and after therapy differences.

The Vision Therapy Achievement Report helps to record the physical and psychological changes that the parents, the teachers, and sometimes the child, observes as the child passes through each phase of Vision Therapy. Many times, in the heat of battle, the changes become lost and it is easy to forget what it was like for the child and the parents before therapy began. Sometimes these changes are shockingly obvious, but oftentimes, they are only measured by success in school, ease at homework time, actual reading level improvement, or an increase in self-confidence.

With the "Achievement Report," the office has an opportunity to share in the triumphs that happen outside of the time we spend with the child. Throughout the time spent with us at the office, it is inevitable that we take a vested interest in the patient, the patient's needs and struggles, and of course, the patient's success. When all of us together, the parents, the child, the therapists, and I actually see improvement, it is a celebration!

Each of these "Achievement Reports," which are filled out at eight to ten week intervals, allows us to make sure the child is reaching the goals we designed for them and allows us to fine tune their personal treatment plan if we need to do so.

We individualize treatment to each child. Some reach goals faster than others depending on their diagnosis. Checking periodically allows us to make adjustments as needed, and this time gives us an opportunity to share in their accomplishments as well. The scheduled time of evaluation and discussion give everyone a chance share observations. Parents also need a time to reflect and ask the doctor questions along the path to success.

Also, if the child knows that his/her performance is being noticed and applauded, that in itself raises their self-esteem and motivation. Constant reinforcement helps parents and children gain more from the program and feel that a competent and concerned staff is meeting their needs.

And as a result, the remaining therapy seems easier and the patient has more incentive to follow through with their home exercises. Of course, this will yield more successful results. It works for everyone!

19 WHERE TO GO FOR HELP?

19 WHERE TO GO FOR HELP?

So, is this your child? Is this the answer for which you've been searching? Vision Therapy might be the solution, and I truly hope you are able to find help and hope for you and your child.

Locating someone that specializes in Vision Therapy in your area might be a challenge, but the Internet can help and there are many resources listed below which provide some excellent information as well as a list of doctors who provide this service.

The Optometric Extension Program Foundation (OEPF), founded in 1928, exists primarily to further education and research in vision. Search for the OEPF on the web for a myriad of other sound resources and information (www.oep.org).

Optometrist Network has been providing advertisement free education on the internet for patients since 1996. See www. visionstories.org.

Another valuable resource for information regarding Vision Therapy is the American Optometric Association or the AOA. Most well educated and skilled optometrists are members of this long established organization of professionals. The website is www.aoa.org

All optometrists are exposed to Vision Therapy to some degree while studying for their Doctor of Optometry degrees. While it is not a major focus, all receive basic introductory information at school. But to become a Vision Therapy specialist, an optometrist must have additional courses of training in this area after the Optometry degree is completed.

Specialists in Vision Therapy are registered and certified with the College of Optometrists in Vision Development or COVD. Certain prerequisites for certification in Vision Development and Vision Therapy follow a three-year waiting period after graduating from optometry school. After this time, the candidate must pass two difficult written exams, present an extensive series of reports documenting Vision Therapy patients and their treatment, and finally, the candidate must be successful in communicating their mastery of the subject to the National Board of the College of Vision Development in an oral examination.

Candidates successful in achieving all of this are given the title of Fellow in the College of Vision Development or FCOVD. A doctor with this qualification can be located by going to www.covd. org/membership. The website is a wealth of information for anything from searching for a qualified doctor, to acquiring more information on the connection between vision and learning, to discovering what vision therapy means for adults just starting on their journey of discovery.

Many qualified vision specialists can be found in all areas of the country, and with a little research and a few strategically asked questions, you can be your child's best advocate in finding help. Have patience with the process and rest assured knowing that help is around the corner.

GLOSSARY OF TERMS
COMPLIMENTS OF OPTOMETRIC EXTENSION PROGRAM

GLOSSARY OF TERMS
COMPLIMENTS OF OPTOMETRIC EXTENSION PROGRAM

Accommodation: An important visual skill that allows us to see clearly at all distances.

Amblyopia: This is also known as "lazy eye", and with this situation sight is below the expected, normal level. Amblyopia results from a problem with the function of the vision system, such as early strabismus or nystagmus. The brain quickly learns to suppress or shut off the processing of input through the "lazy" eye's circuit. Amblyopia at any age can usually be successfully treated by optometric vision therapy. About 2 percent of the general population has it.

Astigmatism: The development of unequal curvature of the cornea. Thus, the light gathered in by the eye is not focused properly.

Binocularity: The simultaneous use of the two eyes in the act of vision.

Binocular vision: The type of vision in which the two eyes are related in their movements so that they are both directed at the same point of regard and each contributes simultaneously to the total perception.

Compensating lens: See minus lens (concave) and plus lens (convex).

Convergence: The act of turning the two eyes inward, toward each other, in order to see a near object. You might be reading or watching a ball move.

Coordination: This refers to the two eyes working together in binocular vision; this is also known as teaming.

Cornea: This is the transparent portion on the front of the eyeball, over the iris and pupil.

Depth perception: Perception of the relief of objects in which they appear to be in three dimensions rather than as flat pictures (see Stereopsis).

Dominant eye: In optometric vision therapy, this is generally described as the "preferred eye". An individual is usually consistent in using the same eye for all responses; it is a response of the motor system, during which the individual aligns either eye toward the object of regard. The preferred eye response usually matches handedness.

Esophoria: This refers to a tendency for one or both eyes to run (over converge) beyond the expected while looking at objects at various distances. The eye(s) will look straight but special tests reveal the tendency to cross.

Esotropia: Also known as an internal squint, in which one or both eyes turn inward (crossed eyes) and can be observed cosmetically.

Exotropia: One or both eyes may turn out, away from one another; this is also know as external squint (wall eyed) and can be observed cosmetically.

Extraocular muscles: The six muscles that guide movement of the eye: internal and external recti, superior and inferior recti, and superior and inferioroblique. The brain controls the voluntary nervous system and thus controls eye movements; the muscles direct eye movements.

Farsightedness: See Hyperopia.

Fixation: Aiming or directing the eyes while shifting rapidly from one object to another, such as reading from word to word on a line, or copying from a textbook to a notebook.

Focus: this function of the vision system identifies information gathered through fixations. The ability of the focusing mechanism to change quickly and accurately while exerting the least amount of energy depends on the individual's stress response. The focusing response is under the control of the involuntary nervous system (autonomic); however, it is possible to gain some control over the focusing function through certain optometric vision therapy procedures.

Form Sense, Form Perception: The ability to organize and recognize visual sensations as shapes, noticing likes and differences (such as the difference between was and saw, that and what). This ability depends on eye movements used during fixations and eye scanning of the visual space around us.

Fusion: a binocular response that simultaneously combines the separate inputs from the two eyes into a single mental image at the brain level (the visual cortex).

Hyperopia (farsightedness): A refractive condition of the eye in which an object can be seen clearly only by using extra accommodation. Small amounts are normal.

Iris: The colored ring surrounding the eye's pupil.

Lens: A transparent, flexible medium with two boundary surfaces, one of which is curved.

Macula: The area at the center of the retina that has clearest vision. The macula contains only cones and does not have any rods.

Minus lens (concave): A lens used traditionally by both ophthalmologists and general optometrists (non-behavioral optometrists) to compensate for myopia. This type of lens compresses the space world, increases the strain on the muscles and encourages rigidity, and thus less flexibility, of both physical movement and mental problem solving.

Myopia: Commonly called nearsightedness. A symptom of a vision imbalance; the myopic individual has difficulty seeing distant objects clearly.

Optic nerve: The main nerve connects the eye to the seeing part of the brain.

Plus lens: A lens traditionally used by both ophthalmologists and general optometrists (non-behavioral optometrists) to compensate for hyperopia (farsightedness). It has the opposite effect of a minus lens (see glossary). In addition to the conventional use of the plus lens, the behavioral optometrist uses it to remediate or nurture an immature vision system and change behavioral responses. Plus lenses are also used as part of optometric vision therapy programs. These lenses are very effective in helping an individual keep their visual system in balance.

Pupil: The opening in the center of the eye through which light passes into the eye.

Refraction: The clinical measurement of the eye to determine the need for lenses; in behavioral optometry this is only one part of the visual analysis to determine the need for lenses.

Retina: The innermost layer of the eye. This is a layer of complex nerve endings upon which light rays are focused; it contains the rod and cone cells.

Retinoscope: This is a hand-held instrument used by professionals in eye care to measure objectivity, the refractive situation.

Sight: The ability to focus and see both at distance and near. The clarity depends on the flexibility of the focusing system and is only one aspect of vision.

Vision, Central: This gives us optimum clarity when we read, play